SILK SCREEN METHODS OF REPRODUCTION

for

Sign Painters, Card Writers, Display Men, Furniture Decorators, Novelty Manufacturers, Glass Etchers and For Domestic Use

By

BERT ZAHN

Fully Illustrated by the Author

CHICAGO
FREDERICK J. DRAKE & CO.
Publishers

Copyright, 1939
By
Frederick J. Drake & Co.
Publishers
Chicago

Printed in the United States of America

CONTENTS

PAGE

FOREWORD 9

CHAPTER

I STENCIL METHODS 13

II EQUIPMENT FOR THE SILK SCREEN
METHOD OF REPRODUCTION . . . 19

III PAINTS USED IN SCREEN WORK . . 36

IV COLOR IN PROCESS WORK 48

V THE COPY 51

VI BLOCKING OR STOPPING OUT THE
SCREEN 53

VII RUNNING THE JOB 57

VIII ESTIMATING THE JOB 60

IX "TROUBLE SHOOTING" WHILE SCREEN-
ING 62

X THE SINGLE SCREEN OR ELIMINATION
PROCESS 64

XI PAPER MASK STENCIL 72

XII THE SINGLE STENCIL METHOD OF RE-
PRODUCTION 74

XIII THE PHOTOGRAPHIC OR SENSITIZED
SCREEN 80

XIV THE PAINT PRESS METHOD OF REPRO-
DUCTION 87

XV PAPER SIGNS, LITHOGRAPHIC IMPRINTS,
ETC. 93

XVI PROCESSING TYPEWRITTEN LETTERS AND
DRAWINGS 97

XVII HOW TO MAKE STICK-ON LETTERS .. 101

XVIII WORKING SURFACES 107

9 / l 0

CONTENTS

CHAPTER		PAGE
XIX	COUNTER OR DOOR GLASS SIGNS . .	110
XX	WINDOW BACKGROUNDS	113
XXI	PROCESSING PENNANTS, FELT ARM-BANDS, ETC.	115
XXII	GLASS SIGNS	120
XXIII	PROCESSING DECALCOMANIA SIGNS .	130
XXIV	HOW TO MAKE SUNLIGHT SIGNS . .	138
XXV	PROCESSING TIRE COVERS	140
XXVI	STENCILS FOR THE HOME	144
XXVII	COMBINATION PROCESS AND ETCHED BRASS SIGNS	148
XXVIII	HANDY SHOP NOTES	149

CONTENTS—PART II

CHAPTER		PAGE
XXIX	THE MIRROR OUTLINE GLASS SIGN .	153
XXX	THE TUSCHE METHOD	160
XXXI	THE CARBON TISSUE METHOD . . .	162
XXXII	THE LACQUER PAPER STENCIL . . .	168
XXXIII	THE PROFILM METHOD	170

CONTENTS—PART III

CHAPTER		PAGE
XXXIV	NU-FILM METHOD	187
XXXV	GLASS SIGNS, ETCHING AND BACK-UP	194
XXXVI	FLOCK AND FLOCK FINISHES . . .	201
XXXVII	TWENTY-FOUR SHEET POSTER . . .	206
XXXVIII	INDIRECT PHOTOGRAPHIC METHOD .	209
XXXIX	CARBON TISSUE METHOD (WET) . .	214
XL	LITHOGRAPHIC OR TUSCHE SCREENS .	220
XLI	MECHANICAL MACHINES FOR PROCESS PRINTING	225
XLII	PAINTS USED IN SCREEN WORK . .	229
	INDEX	234

FOREWORD

THERE is no other phase of the graphic arts which presents so many possibilities as the *Silk Screen Process*. It is adapted to many fields of work other than regular commercial printing. The production of advertising signs and displays forms the field of its greatest commercial use at present. The advantages are so many and the disadvantages so few that advertisers are rapidly finding it the most desirable method for the purpose. It does not supplant lithography but supplements it. It really can be said to have created its own place in advertising. Some even predict that it will in a great measure take the place of lithography for advertising displays and signs because of the added attractiveness and effectiveness of signs made with oil colors.

The silk screen process is being used by a great number of concerns specializing in the manufacture of process signs and displays throughout the world. It is an excellent thing for chain stores. Nearly every chain store organization operating ten or more stores employs its own show card writer or sign man. The type of signs commonly used by these concerns is the paper banner to be pasted on the outside of the window, featuring special items and prices. These are changed frequently, usually two or three times a week, and in this way are always kept fresh and attractive.

The advantages to such organizations of this process are obvious and need no explanation here. They can secure just as attractive posters and banners with this process as they can by hand and a considerable economy is effected.

The silk screen process has many other uses and possibilities. It is being used to a great extent by manufacturers of toys, novelties, wagons and industrial and agricultural machinery of all kinds for placing the trademark, design, patent numbers, etc., on the manufactured article. For this purpose a silk screen has the advantage of making a perfect imprint at low cost. A screen for this purpose will rarely cost the manufacturer more than ten or fifteen dollars and it will last indefinitely, giving many thousands of perfect impressions.

To a great extent it is also used for printing dress silks, fabrics, etc. This class of process printing involves the use of a special printing medium which is usually mixed in the factories' own laboratories. There are no printing mediums obtainable for this purpose in the open market, due principally to the fact that this kind of printing is in the hands of a few and the colors required are not standard. Thousands of colors and color combinations are used for fabric printing, and a manufacturer would have to carry a prohibitive number of colors to meet this demand.

A screen is also being used to a certain extent for printing furs. Imitation leopard skins are made by printing black spots on fur by the use of mediums similar to those used for printing silks. Pillow tops are being turned out in large volume with the silk screen process. This includes pillows made of oilcloth, velvet, satin, and other materials. Of course the design is printed before the material has been made up. Velvet drapes are frequently printed with the silk screen process, as are bridge covers, card tables, gaming cloths, etc.

Women's felt hats are a recent addition to the line of materials being made more attractive when printed with this process. Maps are turned out with the process, principally when only a small quantity is required and it is not necessary that all the details, such as names of towns, rivers, railroads, etc., be shown.

Furniture is being decorated with the silk screen process with increasing popularity, and this includes all classes of furniture, tables, chairs, book-ends, screens, beds, etc. Fibre and cloth rugs are being made with this method in increasing volume. Book and catalog covers are very often attractively produced. Vacuum cleaner manufacturers are printing their dust bags with the process, and under the same classification come newspaper carrier bags, advertising carpenter aprons, caps, etc.

Tire covers are printed with the silk screen process. Twenty-four sheet posters completely printed with the process are coming more and more into general use. Transparent glass and celluloid signs are usually made with the process as well as opaque counter, fountain and display signs in glass. Even halftones have been produced with the photographic method, as well as mimeographed letters and line drawings.

The author, in presenting this book to the public, has endeavored to make it as complete as possible. To supplement his own knowledge and experience in the art he has sought the advice from time to time of the best-known experts in their respective specialized lines. It is impossible to visualize the future developments in this line, but at the time this book goes to press every known method is incorporated. It presents with clear and concise instructions the handling of the process and the various materials used for nearly every known class of work for which it is adaptable.

The author has endeavored to make this impartial and as authoritative as possible. No names of manufacturers are mentioned, although in many cases it has been stated that manufacturers' products are superior to a homemade article. An artist does not attempt to make his own brushes or other materials and articles, so it seems entirely practical to assume that this also holds true in process work. Materials made by specialists in modern factories with modern equipment are superior to a homemade product.

No materials or articles have been mentioned by name, and in any case where a trade-mark has been mentioned, it is solely because it is the only item that will work properly in that particular instance.

FOREWORD TO THIRD EDITION

In *Screen Process,* as in other fields, rapid strides have been made in the development and improvement of operations and ultimate results. The author, instead of rearranging this entire book as developments were made, has added to the original book those improvements most widely and practically used.

With the growth of the industry, other fields have been attracted to it, adding their knowledge to develop machinery, chemicals and formulas that have made *Screen Process* more practical and efficient.

Without the aid and assistance of many individuals in the Process Industry this book would never have been possible and I want to thank my many friends who have so kindly assisted with suggestions, formulas, etc.

THE AUTHOR.

SILK SCREEN METHODS
OF REPRODUCTION

CHAPTER I

STENCIL METHODS

THE method of reproducing designs or lettering by means other than by hand dates back to the early Egyptians. Later the Chinese made tapestries and wall decorations by the method now known as the silk screen method. This is accomplished by blocking out the design on a meshed surface, leaving the copy or design to be reproduced open in the meshes. Paint or color is forced through this screen on to the blank surface upon which the copy is to be produced. In about the year 1900, it was used by the Germans and English in a crude way. It is only in the last ten years that the process has been employed to any great extent to reproduce ordinary lettered signs. Today it is recognized as the only method to reproduce so faithfully most any design in color and appearance that in most cases it cannot be distinguished from an original drawing. In addition, it answers a need for a method to supply in limited quantities the displays that otherwise would prove prohibitive in cost were color printing plates made.

Since it is the intention of this book to cover the entire field of making signs or displays in quantity by other than hand methods, some of the commoner methods should be mentioned.

OIL PAPER OR STRAIGHT STENCIL

We will commence with one of the oldest, the oil paper, or straight, stencil. Either one or a series of stencils can be used. With the single stencil, ties or holders are used to keep the letters and centers from falling out or breaking when stenciling. In other words, these ties are used simply to strengthen the letters. Fig. 1

PROCESS

Figure 1.—A Single Stencil.

shows a single stencil with the laps or ties in the most desirable spots to make a strong stencil. When stenciled, these laps will have to be filled in by hand. This necessitates hand labor, which we are trying to eliminate, therefore a double stencil is far the better method.

DOUBLE STENCIL

We will assume that you have made the sketch for a double-stencil lettering design and that you are ready to reproduce it. First take two sheets of stencil paper, or if this is unobtainable, heavy butcher paper will do for small quantities or "runs." Lay the stencil paper on your table and upon this place a sheet of carbon paper, carbon side down. On this place another sheet of stencil paper and on this another sheet of carbon paper. On these lay your copy (sketch) and tack all sheets on to your board or base. With a sharp stencil knife cut out the "markers," which are small corners or portions of a letter on each end, top and bottom. These should be cut through all five sheets. Care must be taken to get a sharp edge as registration will be difficult if the edges are ragged or irregular. After markers are cut, trace the entire copy. Remove carbons and treat each sheet of the stencil paper with a coat of raw oil. When this is dry, coat both sides with shellac. You are now ready to cut the stencil. Use the heaviest copy first and cut out the first

Figure 2.—Double Stencil, First Cut.

half of the letters. Only by experimenting will you know which portion to cut out first, due to the variations in letters and types used. For example, see Fig. 2. The black portions are the parts to be cut out on the first stencil. As a cutting base use a sheet of zinc or glass. The best knife is the regular stencil blade mounted in a handle or regular knife which can be purchased at any

Figure 3.—Double Stencil, Second Cut.

paint store. This must always be sharp with a good point. Always cut on an inward slope as this will prevent the paint from seeping under when stenciling. When this first stencil is cut, place it on top of the remaining sheet, registering with cut-out portions, and tack down. Stencil this cut-out stencil onto the remaining sheet, then cut out this stencil. The reason for stenciling is to show you just where your letters leave off, allowing you to get a perfect overlap. Fig. 3 shows the second cutting operation. Your stencil is now ready for "running."

STENCILING

In stenciling, it is best to use a pure oil color in paste form, as japan colors dry and have a tendency to leave a rough edge on the stencil. Dry colors can be used by mixing with boiled oil and a little dryer. This should be in paste form for if it is too thin, it will run under the stencil, leaving a rough edge.

Place the paint on a sheet of glass or metal and dip your stencil brush (No. 200 or 300 preferred) into it and work it out on the glass so as to mix it properly.

Figure 4.—First Cut of Reverse Background Stencil.

Lay the first stencil on the cardboard, paper or other working surface, placing weights on it to prevent shifting. With a circular motion proceed to stencil, being sure that the register marks are sharp. A felt roller may also be used instead of a stencil brush. When your first run (stenciled sheet) is dry, place the second stencil on the first run, registering with markers, weight and stencil this. This completes the sign.

REVERSE BACKGROUND STENCILS

When the background is to be stenciled instead of the letters, the stencil is cut out just the opposite of the cut-out letters. The obstacle to avoid in cutting this stencil is sharp edges or corners. Always cut stencils in such a way that there are no protruding edges, as these will be torn or bent in stenciling. Fig. 4 gives a good idea of the proper method of cutting the first stencil. Fig. 5

Figure 5.—Second Stencil (Reverse).

shows the second stencil. All operations are the same as in the preceding section. Fig. 6 shows the completed copy. It is advisable never to pounce in stenciling as

Figure 6.—Completed Copy from Reverse Background Stencil.

the stencil is easily torn. When not in use, keep stencil brushes wrapped in paper and suspended in a solution of half turpentine and half linseed oil.

RUNNING TWO OR MORE COLORS AT THE SAME TIME

In case the design is in more than one color, a paper mask on hinges is employed for each color. This is lowered when the black is being stenciled and raised when stenciling the red. Always leave enough space between lines as colors are apt to run together.

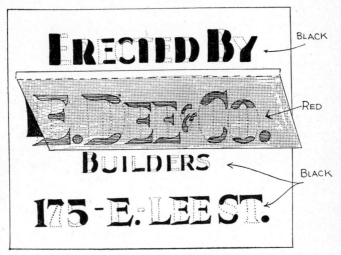

Figure 7.—A Two-Color Stencil.

CHAPTER II

EQUIPMENT FOR THE SILK SCREEN METHOD OF REPRODUCTION

B Y SILK screen process is meant the forcing of paint or color through the open meshes of a screen or fabric whereon is painted or "blocked" a design to be reproduced—or "processed."

The amount of space and equipment required to start depends upon the scope of business anticipated, whether large or small. It is advisable for the beginner to start on a small scale, working to a bigger business, and not, as has been the failing of many, to invest in a large amount of equipment and supplies with insufficient returns in view.

The first item required is the unit, or process, table. Any good strong table, well braced, and from 36 to 40 inches high, is suitable. Next is the base, and this is one of the most important items, because a slight deviation or unevenness in it will obviously cause considerable trouble.

The best size of board for a base is 36 by 46 inches, and this is ample for a sheet of 22 by 28 inches or less. Of course, in case of larger jobs, a larger base and unit are necessary. With several bases and units of different sizes, more than one job can be handled at the same time, but as a model and for our first job, which is 22 by 28 inches, our base will be 36 by 46 inches. It is best to have a cabinetmaker or carpenter build it, but the handy

man can build his own. Kiln-dried lumber is best and
should be laminated in at least two layers. See Fig. 8.

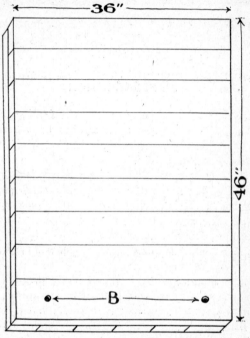

Figure 8.—A Laminated Base.

THE SINGLE-BAR STRETCHER FRAME

The size of the frame to fit the base mentioned should
be 24 by 30 inches, inside measurement, and made of perfect 2-by-3-inch kiln-dried cypress or basswood lumber.
The inside measurement of 30 inches is taken from the
floating bar to the inside bottom of the frame, giving
an outside measurement of the frame of 38 by 30 inches.
In other words, this would be the size of the frame
proper. See Fig. 9.

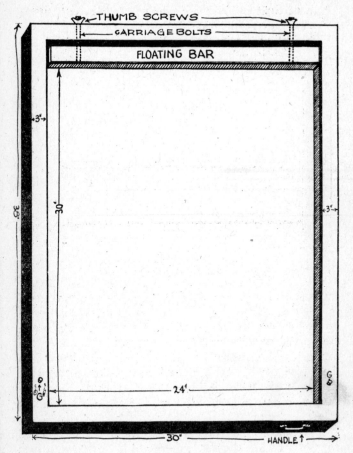

Figure 9.—The Frame.

The simplest method of attaching the silk to the frame is tacking. But it is advisable to use grooves and strips if the frame is intended for long use. The grooves are ½ inch deep, cut as shown in Fig. 10. Wood strips are cut to fit tight into these grooves and holes are drilled for screws every 3 inches.

The floating bar is 23½ inches long and is also made of 2-by-3-inch lumber with the grooves running into the

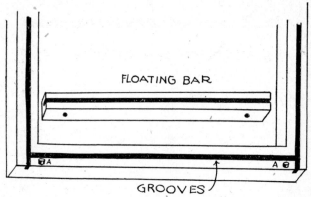

Figure 10.—Frame with Grooves.

extreme ends. The wood strips are cut the same length as the bar. The floating bar is fastened to the frame proper by two carriage bolts, 8 inches long, with square heads and equipped with thumbscrews. Fig. 11 shows the bar in place on the frame, holes having been drilled into the frame for the bolts. The heads of the bolts are on the inside of the floating bar, these having been counter-sunk so that the heads of the bolts are flush with the wood.

Place on the groove side of the frame two hard-wood pegs ½ inch in diameter. These are to protrude ½ inch and are set into the frame ½ inch. Fig. 10, *A* shows location of pegs. These pegs are to fit holes in the base and will prevent shifting of the frame when running, thus giving a perfect register even if hinges should loosen.

Now turn the frame over, and on the side without the

grooves place two metal pins ½ inch in diameter, to stick up 1 inch. These are to be placed 4½ inches from the bottom of the frame. Fig. 9, *G*. These pegs are to hold

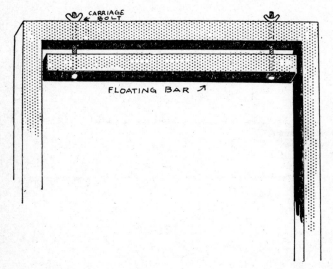

Figure 11.—Reverse Side of Frame with Floating Bar.

the squeegee when the screen is in use, preventing the paint from running over the screen. The frame is now ready to mount on the base.

Lay the frame on the center of the base, groove side down, and mark off places where holes are to be drilled

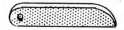

Figure 12.—Automatic Frame Holder.

for the pegs. Drill these holes so that the pegs fit snug (not tight). Fasten the frame to the base with two hinges, which must be of the pin type, which permit you to remove the peg and take the frame off of the base without disturbing the hinge proper.

The automatic arm is to be made next. This holds

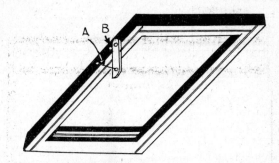

Figure 13.—Frame with Automatic Arm in Position.

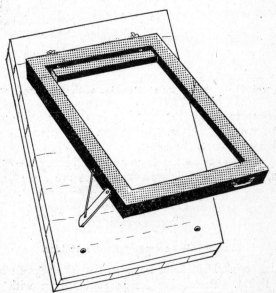

Figure 14.—The Completed Unit, Base and Frame.

the frame up while the paper is being changed during the printing process. Saw a 6-inch piece of 1-by-2-inch lumber and cut it as in Fig. 12. Drill a hole in this and fasten it to the frame as shown in Fig. 13. A rubber band is stretched, *A*, and a screw is placed as *B*, to prevent the arm from going back too far. The completed unit is shown in Fig. 14.

COUNTERBALANCED FRAMES

To make running easier and eliminate raising and lowering the screen by hand for each copy, the frame is counterbalanced with weights on the ends or with pulleys

Figure 15.—Frame with Counterweights.

and weights. Fig. 15 shows the frame with weights on the ends holding the frame in the "ready" or up position

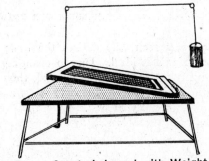

Figure 16.—Frame Counterbalanced with Weight and Pulley.

until it is lowered. When pressure is taken off of the frame, it will automatically rise to the up position.

Fig. 16 shows the frame with a rope and pulley which can be attached with a snap catch. When the frame is lowered the snap automatically catches and holds the frame rigid. This can be released with the foot lever,

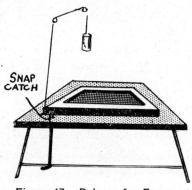

Figure 17.—Release for Frame.

Fig. 17. As all frames may not be of the same weight, these weights will have to be regulated to handle the particular frame you may be using.

THE 4-FLOATING BAR SURE-REGISTER FRAME

For the process man who desires the best, a special 4-floating bar frame is ideal. Due to changing weather, the silk screen is apt to shrink or expand, thus throwing colors badly out of register. In some cases new screens have to be made because of this. With the 4-bar frame there are eight adjustments and in most cases the screen can be adjusted to register colors perfectly. This adjustable frame is made on the same principle as the smaller frame, only that it has four bars instead of one. Fig. 18 shows this unit, and if properly constructed, it will make an ideal foolproof unit.

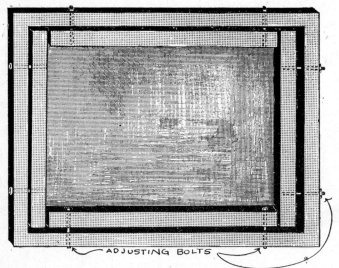

Figure 18.—Four-Floating Bar Frame.

THE SCREEN

There are several kinds of material that can be used for screens, namely, organdy, silk bolting cloth, wire mesh screen, etc. Organdy is the cheapest and will answer in some cases, but for real clean work, bolting cloth is the best. This bolting cloth may be purchased from advertisers in any sign or art trade magazine. Silk bolting cloth is a special fabric which is exceedingly strong, allowing tight stretching without tearing. The weave of this fabric is almost perfect with threads running in even lines. The designating numbers are governed by the amount of mesh to the square inch. The lower numbers have the coarser mesh, the higher numbers being finer. The fine mesh is advisable for finer work and in small lettering and the more delicate designs.

For all around process work the most suitable silk is

the number 13XX, the price of which is approximately
$7 per yard. It comes 40 inches wide. Special widths
may be had but they are not standard.

STRETCHING THE FRAME

First, take the frame from the base by removing pins
from hinges. Loosen the thumbscrews on top of the
floating bar. Lay the silk over the frame on the side
with the groove, Fig. 19, tacking it on four corners,

Figure 19.—Stretching the Silk.

then force the sticks down into the grooves, starting at
the bottom or side opposite the floating bar. Screw the
bar down, then do the opposite side or the floating bar,
and the remaining two sides. Now tighten up on the
thumbscrews, thus tightening the silk. The corners of
the silk may tear a little, but this will have no bad effects
in running.

It must be remembered that silk must be tight to secure the best results. The inside of the frame should
then be lined with gummed tape and gummed tape should

also be placed on the bottom. This is to prevent the paint from leaking through. The completed unit ready for the copy should now appear as in Fig. 20. The markers should be permanent, although some process men use a different marker for each job.

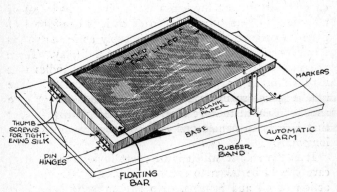

Figure 20.—Unit Ready for the Copy.

For the permanent marker, secure a piece of metal 3 inches long, 1¾ inches wide and ¹⁄₁₆ inch thick. This should be made with an inward bevel in the center so that a flat head screw when affixed will be flush with the top.

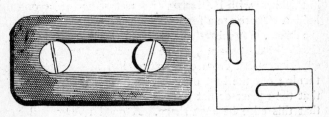

Figure 21.—Markers.

The corner marker is L-shaped and made the same. Fig. 21 gives a good idea of these. The unit is now ready for use, but first let us describe the other equipment, such as drying racks, flood light box, squeegee, etc.

THE SQUEEGEE

It is of the utmost importance that any processor who expects to turn out first-class work give a good deal of attention to the squeegee. Too often it is considered of little importance, whereas it is probably as important as any item entering into the production of a display. There are various styles and shapes of squeegee handles that may be made or procured in the open market. The handle is not so important as the rubber, although care should be taken to have the rubber mounted in a holder that is easy to handle and least tiresome to operate on long runs.

It is the rubber which is of great importance. Great care should be taken to secure a rubber that resists the action of oil and benzine. No rubber made is entirely resistant to the action of oils, but some are better than others in this respect. Secure the best. It is usually impossible to purchase a rubber of this kind from a rubber supply house, but it may be secured from supply houses catering to the process trade.

The rubber should be, for best results, about ⅜ inch in thickness with 1½ inches or more projecting beyond the holder. There are a few process workers who cut or sand the squeegee to a beveled edge, but this is a practice which should be discouraged, as the author has found from long experience and from observation in many process shops turning out the best of work and with the least trouble that the square or flat edge is best. It is very important that this edge be kept sharp. A good rubber will keep a sharp edge for a long time, and when it does become rounded off after much use, it may be resharpened.

This is done by grasping the squeegee holder with both hands (or if the squeegee be a long one, a man holding each end of the squeegee) and rubbing it over a piece of garnet cloth which has been fastened to a table or solid base. The squeegee is held perfectly upright, so that the blade rests squarely on the garnet cloth, and it is then rubbed over the cloth for a few strokes, enough to place a sharp, square edge on the rubber blade.

Care should be taken to exert a uniform pressure along the entire length of the squeegee, otherwise it will not sand uniformly and will have waves in it. The rubber should be neither too soft nor too stiff. The flexibility should be such that when the operator grasps the squeegee holder firmly in his hand and tilts it to an angle of about 45 degrees, it is possible to bend the rubber blade just slightly by exerting ordinary pressure. The pressure should be firm, however, in order to secure a perfect impression and a clean wipe-off. It is only by paying close attention to the squeegee stroke, flexibility of the rubber and the condition of the rubber edge that the paint is forced through the silk perfectly and a uniform impression secured.

Squeegee holders or handles can be made from three pieces of wood, as shown in Fig. 22, *B* being two metal

Figure 22.—The Squeegee.

pins which are driven into each end, these resting on the pins on the frame proper when running. It will be found that this method of holding the squeegee while changing cards is quite a trouble saver, for without them, the squeegee would slide down over the screen when in the up position.

THE DRYING RACK

As space is usually limited in the average shop, the question of racking arises, especially if the order be a large one. On starting in the process business, I found myself with an order for a thousand signs with a very small space to work in, let alone room for drying. The rack I will describe solved the problem. One rack which takes a space of 3 by 9 feet will hold 400 signs 22 by 28

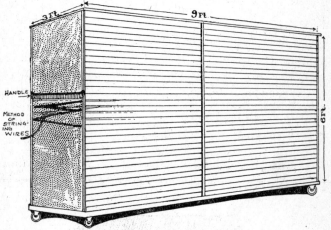

Figure 23.—The Drying Rack.

inches. Fig. 23 gives a clear idea as to the method of construction. The base or truck is built of 2 by 4 lumber with a good roller, preferably of the rubber-tire type. This makes it easy to roll from the process table to an out-of-the-way corner to dry. The uprights are of 2 by 4 lumber and should be well braced, because when the wires are stretched, the strain is apt to loosen the uprights, resulting in loose wire. The rack is 9 feet long, 3 feet wide and 6 feet high above the rollers or trucks. Fig. 24 shows two of the four sections, the cross pieces

being made of ¾-by-1½-inch lumber on which the wires
B are strung.   Any good wire will do with the exception
of copper wire, which will stretch and then sag.   Each
section will hold fifty full sheet cards, and as they are put
in from both sides, a total of 400 cards can be handled.

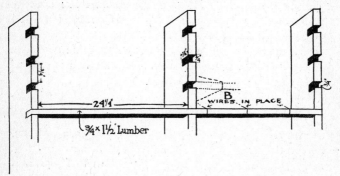

Figure 24.—Two Sections of Drying Rack.

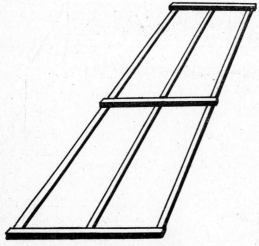

Figure 25.—A Rack Slab.

Another method of racking is to use rack slabs. They are constructed of light lumber ¼ by 1 inch. The size will have to be made to conform with the size of work in hand, but it is best to make them large enough to hold a 28-by-24-inch card. Fig. 25 shows the construction with three cross sections. If six cross sections are used, it will be stronger and small cards can be racked as well as thin paper streamers.

These slabs are placed on a dolly, or movable platform, and can be rolled around at will. This method is in general use in most process houses.

FLOOD LIGHT BOX

A very handy item is a light box, or working base, whereon the screen proper is made. It will be found that when making a screen the mesh may seem to be covered or filled, and when held to the light, it will be found to

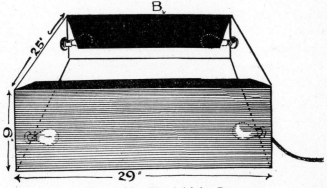

Figure 26.—Flood Light Box.

be full of pinholes, necessitating a lot of tedious retouching. The flood light box is used to show up these pinholes when working on the screen, enabling one to make a perfect screen without retouching. The outside measurements of the box are 25 by 29 inches and 6 inches high. Either two or four lights are used and a piece of frosted glass is placed over this to diminish the glare. Reflectors to throw the light down are mounted over the lights to offset the glare. Fig. 26. This device will answer a two-fold purpose as it can be used when sensitizing or making photographic screens.

CHAPTER III

PAINTS USED IN SCREEN WORK

IT IS folly to think it possible to obtain good results with ordinary paint, as it is not properly ground and may contain ingredients that work well with a brush but will not go through the silk. Process paint should be purchased from a paint store catering to the process trade, as these paints are made for this purpose after careful study and research by the manufacturers. The strength of color in these special paints will be found to be greater, having better covering qualities. Not only this, but these colors can be used exactly as received, without a lot of mixing. The price is a little higher, but the ordinary job will not need full strength color, so that it can be let down with extenders, thereby reducing the cost.

Colors ground in oil are advisable, but japan colors can be used if retarded with a mixture of linseed oil and varnish with a little kerosene. Straight japan colors will clog the screen after two or three copies are run. A good paint will run over the screen easily and will not require a lot of pressure on the squeegee, and will allow the processed display to drop easily from the screen. In case the regular process paint is unobtainable and you have a rush job, the ordinary dull or velvet-finish wall paint will answer the purpose if allowed to stand overnight and the oil removed from the top and a little litho varnish is added. If the paint is made from dry colors, a coarser mesh screen is necessary, using boiled oil, body varnish, and litho varnish with a few drops of kerosene. Show card colors or water colors are usable, but must be mixed with mucilage and glycerine. Some screen men even use molasses or honey to retard the rapid drying qualities of these colors. There is on the market a solution that may be used fairly well to mix with show card or water colors. But with the beautiful effects that are obtainable with oil colors, it is folly to try to use any other.

Printing inks can be used, especially if a transparent effect is desired, such as on shades, celluloid, glass, isinglass, etc. In using printing ink a color combination is possible, such as in color process printing, getting a four or five-color effect with the use of but three colors. Colors for such jobs should be placed one on another before the previous color is entirely dry. Process japan may be added to hasten drying. In dusting on bronzes this will be found very satisfactory, the ink becoming tacky in from three to four hours.

As color is so important to the process industry, it is necessary to understand and know the treatment and application of the raw materials. Following is an outline of some of the properties, treatments and uses of materials generally used in making paints for screen process work.

The specifications of an ideal paint for process work would be difficult to make up and one specification would never cover all the requirements for different work. The specification for a paint for screen process work usually includes the following requirements:

1. Shade of color—depth and brilliance
2. Finish—flat, satin or gloss
3. Drying time—oxidation and penetration
4. Covering capacity—opaque or transparent

5. Durability—outside or inside exposure
6. Permanence—fastness to light

The requirements of a paint vary according to the work to be done, and with the many applications of the screen process method, it is impossible to make a paint for more than a few uses. Paints are being applied by this process to the following materials: paper, cardboard, wood, glass, steel, oilcloth, canvas, satin, silk, parchment, etc.

To meet all these requirements, the manufacturer is making many entirely different types of paints by using different treatments of oils, varnishes, etc., and various pigment combinations to obtain the desired working properties and results. Therefore, a short listing of some of these treatments and properties should be of interest.

RAW MATERIALS

The raw materials entering into the manufacture of paint are divided into the following general classes:

Vehicles—oils, varnishes, thinners, driers
Pigments—whites, blacks and inerts
Colors—earths, chemicals and dyes

All manufacturers use practically the same materials and obtain results by approximately the same treatment and combination of vehicle and pigment in paint making. In the following listing the general treatment and properties are given for the common raw materials used for process paints:

VEHICLES

1. *Linseed Oil* is by far the most common and best oil used in these paints. It is used as a grinding and mix-

ing oil. As raw linseed oil does not dry within 36 hours, it is generally heat treated in a varnish kettle to 500° F. and small quantities of driers (lead or manganese) added to it as desired. This is called "boiling oil." Linseed oil is also heat treated to make bleached oil and enamel oil for use in white paints, etc., to preserve color and easy working paints. Continued heating of the oil increases the body and "tack," and also adds to the flexibility and durability of the dried film. Many resins and other oils are combined with linseed oil by heat to produce "mixing varnishes," finishing varnishes and spar varnish. These combinations are made in order to effect quick or hard drying, pigment absorption, gloss or flat finish, length or shortness and weather-resisting properties to the paint.

2. *China Wood Oil* is an imported oil which is used in varnish making. It cannot be used in the raw state and must be heat treated in the varnish kettle. It is then more waterproof than linseed oil and can be made to dry very rapidly and hard. It is used in a large percentage of grinding varnishes and produces very satisfactory results. In some varnishes it produces a flat finish when ground with pigments and this makes a most durable paint. It produces easy working and hard drying paints, and is generally as expensive as linseed oil, and for some paints produces better results.

3. *Rosin,* a derivative of the sap secretion of the pine tree, is used in making varnishes for mixing, etc., but does not find a very wide use in process paints. It is not waterproof and a large percentage of it increases the brittleness of the varnish in which it is used. Rosin is used in small percentage to temper China wood oil and varnishes to produce drying, setting and other working properties.

4. *Gums.*—Many grades of fossil and synthetic gums are used in varnish making and according to the grade, produce different finishes and durable films. The gen-

eral purpose of gums in varnish is to increase the toughness, adhesion and durability of the oil with which they are used.

5. *Driers* are materials which have the property of helping oils, varnishes, etc., absorb oxygen to produce a hard film. The metals, cobalt, lead, and manganese are the principal driers in use and these are incorporated in varnishes, japans, oil driers and paste driers, according to where they are to be used. The drying strength of a drier varies with the percentage of the metals in solution in the drier. A minimum quantity of drier should be used to produce the desired results, as an excess generally produces discoloration and shortens the durability of the varnish or oil film.

6. *Thinners.*—Turpentine, naphtha and kerosene are the common thinners used in process paints, and with these one can produce all the desired results. Turpentine is generally used in thinning the coating and spar varnishes. There are many grades of naphtha in use, and according to the speed of evaporation of the naphtha, the setting of the paint or varnish can be regulated as desired. Kerosene is a slow thinner and increases the penetration of the paint.

PIGMENTS

1. *White Lead* is one of the main pigments used in process paints because it is durable, white, and it has great covering capacity. Outdoor paints generally contain a large percentage of white lead.

2. *Zinc Oxide* is used with white lead and other pigments because of its pure whiteness and easy working properties.

3. *Lithopone* is a precipitated product composed of zinc sulphide and varium sulphate. It is a good covering pigment and is used to produce white and other paints for process work.

4. *Titanium Oxide* is a comparatively new pigment, used because of its very great covering capacity. It is more expensive than the other white pigments and is used in special process paints.

5. *Blanc Fix* and *Barytes* are white pigments composed of barium sulphate and are used as inert pigment in paints. By themselves they are not opaque. They add weight and shortness to a paint and are inactive and durable.

6. *Asbestine* is a white pigment used to prevent a paint from settling hard. It is not opaque and is used in limited quantities. It is magnesium silicate.

7. *Whiting* is calcium carbonate, a white pigment used as an extender; it works short in paint. Magnesia, talc, gypsum, silica, and numerous other white powders are used in paint-making, each for a particular property which they impart to the paint.

COLORS

Colors used in paint making for screen process work are classed in four groups, namely: earth colors, chemical colors, lake colors and dyes. These classes are so divided because of the method of manufacture for each color. Other classifications can be made, such as opaque, transparent, fast, fugitive, etc., but these properties are regulated to a great degree by manipulation and grinding. Purity of a color is as essential to the user of paint as it is to the manufacturer and the covering capacity and tinting value of a color are generally proportional to the percentage of coloring matter present.

1. *Earth Colors* include all colors which are found as natural deposits and put through various purifying, washing and grinding operations to procure uniform clean shades. These colors are generally soft shades and are quite permanent to light.

A. *Sienna* is a fairly soft earth composed of silicates

colored with varying percentages of iron hydrate and oxide naturally present. The two shades, raw and burnt, have fair tinting strength and produce ivory, tan, buffs and brown shades. They are permanent to light and stable compounds.

B. *Umber* is similar to sienna in composition and contains some manganese in addition to iron as the coloring matter. Raw and burnt umber have fair tinting strength and make tan, browns and soft neutral shades with green, blue, etc.

C. *Ochre* is another soft silicate earth colored by iron hydrate, which is permanent to light and a stable compound. Ochres are all low in tinting strength and generally more of a yellow shade than raw sienna.

D. *Indian Red* is a natural earth colored by a higher percentage of iron oxide. It is a dull bluish red and produces a dirty rose tint. It is permanent to light.

E. *Red Oxides* are earths containing various percentages of iron oxide as coloring matter and of various degrees of brilliance. Some of these oxides are called Venetian reds and all are permanent to light and do not make clean tints.

F. *Van Dyke Brown* is a dark brown earth, which does not have much tinting strength and is not generally used in grinding paints.

2. *Chemical Colors* are those colored pigments manufactured by chemicals by precipitation and chemical reaction.

A. *Iron Oxides* of very high grade are made by roasting and precipitation and are very permanent to light and make more brilliant shades than the natural oxides. They are generally strong in tinting strength.

B. *Iron Hydrate* is a manufactured product similar in shade to ochre and very much stronger in tinting strength. It is permanent and stable.

C. *Chrome Yellows* are precipitated colors containing

lead chromate, lead sulphate and lead carbonate in varying percentages. There are innumerable shades of chrome yellow produced, but generally the following are the standard shades: primrose, light or lemon (sometimes called strontia), medium or chrome and orange chrome yellow. All these colors have very good covering capacity and are permanent to light, but all shades darken on long exposure outdoors. Primrose shades with peacock and milori blue make the cleanest, brightest greens. Light chrome yellow produces canary shade tints; medium chrome produces buffs and orange for flesh, etc.

D. *Zinc Yellow* is a very light greenish shade and is very permanent and alkali proof. It is excellent for making leaf green and brilliant shades.

E. *Cadmium Yellow* is really an artist color composed of cadmium sulphide and is absolutely permanent but expensive.

F. *Vermilion* is a sulphide of mercury and a very heavy pigment. It is permanent and has great covering capacity. It is costly and a pure vermilion paste would be hard to work on a screen.

G. *Orange Mineral* is an oxide of lead and is a very brilliant orange of good covering capacity. It is a very heavy pigment and permanent to light.

H. *Paris Green* is a very brilliant, fast shade of green containing lead and arsenic. It is a light pigment and fair in covering capacity. As it is poisonous its use is limited.

I. *Chrome Green* is a combination of chrome yellow and Prussian blue, and is made in a great many shades, but generally three, light, medium and deep. These are permanent to light and very high in covering capacity. The shade varies with the amount of yellow present with blue.

J. *Prussian Blue* is a name generally applied to ferric

ferocyanide blues. This pigment is very fast to light and has great tinting strength. Dry color manufacturers are making a number of shades of this color, but generally hold to the following classifications:

> Prussian Blue, darker, redder shade, dense color
>
> Bronze Blue, dark, red toptone and green undertone
>
> Chinese Blue, pure blue shade
>
> Milori Blue, blue toptone and greenish shade tints.

These blues are identical in composition and permanence and each is suited for a specific use.

K. *Ultramarine Blue* and *Cobalt Blue* are made by roasting different chemicals together and are permanent to light and are fair in covering capacity. Cobalt blue is made by adding zinc oxide to the ingredients in making ultramarine blue.

L. *Carbon Black* is made by burning natural gas in an insufficient supply of oxygen and collecting the residue and grading it. This is a very light pigment of great covering capacity and tinting strength.

M. *Lamp Black* is made by burning natural crude oil and collecting the residue. It is permanent and heavier than carbon black and bluer in shade.

N. *Drop Black,* or *Ivory Black,* is a residue obtained in roasted bones or ivory. It is a very black pigment and has good working properties.

3. *Lake Colors* include colors made from dyestuffs precipitated as pure color or on a base to make them insoluble in water. According to the dye these colors can be made on a transparent or semi-opaque base and varying strengths of color can be produced. These colors are generally brilliant shades and only a few of the great number produced are permanent to light. In testing lake

colors, manufacturers fix a seal of permanence to light arrived at by testing in a violet ray exposing apparatus. In the following outline, figures will be given for some colors in use at present, using 100 as the figure for Toluidine Toner, the permanent standard.

A. *Toluidine Red* is made in any strength from pure color down to 5 per cent color on different bases such as barytes, whiting, hydrate, etc. It is the best red for outdoor signs and is non-bleeding. It is a yellowish light red and permanence 100.

B. *Fire Red* and *Red Lake* are similar to toluidine in shade and a little brighter or cleaner, but the covering capacity and tinting strength are not quite as good. Permanence 95. They are non-bleeding.

C. *Litho Red* is a dense red made in three shades and varying strengths. It is very opaque and has good tinting strength. It is fairly clean but makes dull tints. Permanence·90. It will bleed under some conditions.

D. *Para Red is* made in two shades, but the deepest shade is used mostly. It is made in various strengths, has great covering capacity, and is not clean by itself or in tints. It bleeds very badly and has permanence of 75.

E. *Scarlets* are made of several different dyes and are all clean shades of average depth, but do not have much covering capacity. Most of them are non-bleeding and permanence of 70 to 80.

F. *Eosin Lakes* are very brilliant reds with a very bluish undertone and produce clean pink tints. They have great tinting strength and are quite transparent. Permanence 35 to 40.

G. *Crimson Lakes* are made of several different dyes and strengths. There are three in popular demand which have great tinting value and are very clean shades; used in making tints of pink, magenta, heliotrope, etc. They cover very well and have a permanence of 40 to 50.

H. *Alizarine Lakes* are being produced in a number of shades such as madder crimson, violet, purple, etc., and are very clean colors though not very strong for tinting. They are non-bleeding and have a permanence of 90 to 100.

I. *Orange Toner* is a very strong brilliant color for tinting, etc., and has good covering capacity. It is non-bleeding and has permanence of 90.

J. *Yellow* and *Orange Lake* are clean brilliant colors being used for greens, flesh tints, etc., and are transparent colors with permanence of 60.

K. *Green Lakes* and *Emerald Green* are made in several shades and strengths. Some green toners are pure color and have great tinting strength and permanence. The average color is semi-transparent and has a permanence of 40 to 50.

L. *Blue Lakes,* such as peacock and turquoise, are made in various strengths and are clean brilliant shades. They make brilliant greens with primrose yellow and have a permanence of 35.

M. *Violet* and *Purple* are used in two strengths of color, the toners and lakes, and very brilliant shades can be had. They cover well and have a permanence of 40 to 50 respectively.

N. *Dyes* are used very little in paints for screen work because they are soluble in oil or water and will bleed or discolor. There are very few permanent dyes. The average will fade in a few days' sun exposure.

From this brief outline of materials used in making screen process paints, the buyer and user of these products can very easily realize that he will obtain the best results if he will acquaint himself with his own particular requirements and then go to a manufacturer and give his specifications. The paint manufacturer is then limited by your specifications and can produce two or three paints to meet them and then determine which is the best working and economical paint for you to use. Paint making is not guesswork; it is a science, and manufacturers are retaining skilled men to make products for specific uses.

CHAPTER IV

COLOR IN PROCESS WORK

COLOR is one of the most important factors in process work which is really founded on the use of color. There are certain principles and rules in the use of colors which will aid one materially in producing displays that are not only arresting to the eye but are pleasing as well. Colors are used not only to attract but also to hold the eye and draw attention to the other portions of the advertising display that the advertiser wishes to have read. The improper use of color may overemphasize one certain portion of the display, leaving the important or explanatory portions of reading matter or design unnoticed. There are various color plans and charts on the market, but there is none, in my opinion, that can compare with the Earhart color plan. In combining colors there are two schemes or harmonies that should be known, the harmony of colors that are related and colors opposite or not related. Any two colors that are related will contain the same visible colors used. In other words, each contains a portion of the base of the other, such as red and orange, red and purple, blue and green, blue and violet, etc. The key color, or point of interest, is usually the heaviest as a matter of attraction. It will be found that a color on a white surface will appear darker than if the same color were used on a dark surface, and when used on a tinted or colored surface, the color will take on another shade. As Earhart says: "All harmonious effects in the arts are obtained only through different elements of contrast. In fact, the nature or value of every single thing which makes an impression upon the mind of man, through any of his senses, is measured by contrast of other things in the same class, or possessing the same qualities. This measurement or judgment may be conscious or subconscious, but it is ever present every time we express ourselves about the nature, character, or quality of anything. This brings the word contrast in use and it is important indeed."

The art of color is a deeply scientific subject generally based upon foundation of certain primary or basic colors of the spectrum. As far as pigments or paints are concerned, many, but not all, agree that red, yellow and any blue are to be considered the primary colors. These primary or basic colors are those that cannot be obtained by mixing other colors. Black and white are not generally considered colors although, of course, they are most important pigments in practical work. It is interesting to note that black may be made with a deep blue-green and a deep red. This does not produce a jet black but a black hue.

With a careful handling of color, beautiful effects can be obtained, even violating the harmony of color. A good example of this is found in theatrical posters. Below will be found a handy chart on colors and how they are obtained by combining pigments.

Brown, three parts red, two yellow, three black
Bottle green, dutch pink, Prussian blue, yellow lake
Claret, carmine and ult. blue
Cream, five parts white, two yellow, one red
Citron, three parts red, two yellow, one part blue
Chestnut, one part black, two red, two chrome yellow
Canary, yellow white tinted down with lemon yellow

Copper, one part red, one part black

Drab, nine parts white, one part burnt umber

Flesh, eight parts white, three vermilion, three chrome yellow

French gray, white tinted with ivory black

Gold Color, white and chrome orange tinted with red and a touch of blue

Lemon, five parts white to two parts lemon yellow

Lilac, four parts red, three white, one blue (ult.)

Maroon yellow, three parts carmine, two parts yellow

Olive, chrome yellow dark, tinted with black, adding a touch of red and blue

Pea Color, five parts white, one chrome green medium.

CHAPTER V

THE COPY

THE first article necessary for screen work is the original or master sketch from which the duplicates are to be made. It is advisable to make only a rough sketch and merely indicate various color combinations. This eliminates the time in making a completely finished drawing. It may appear strange but it seems to be a proven fact that the average advertising buyer will O.K. a rough sketch more readily than a completed design.

It is wise in making sketches to eliminate colors that are not fast or colors that will bleed. Beautiful effects may be obtained, it is true, but plenty of trouble may be encountered when screening. Not only this, but colors of an aniline base are fadable and will not hold up under the sun.

For the first job we are to run, we will select a simple three-color straight lettering run. Fig. 27 is to be our copy.

The first step is to trace the copy onto the screen. As this is the first job on a new equipment, several operations are necessary that will not have to be done on future runs, namely, the placing of markers, adjusting the pin hinges, etc. Place the master copy on the base, preferably in the exact center, and tack temporarily. On the left bottom side place markers as well as on the right bottom. See Fig. 28. These markers are cut either from cardboard or fibre or they may be of metal with rounded top edges that will not cut the screen while running. These

Figure 27.—Copy for Three-Color Lettering Job.

markers are fastened to the base with screws and are permanent. When markers are fastened, remove tacks, place screen on base and fasten with the pin hinges. Place the

Figure 28.—Placing Markers.

master copy in position and trace it on the screen, using a medium hard pencil, not too sharp or it will cut the silk. When traced, remove screen from base and place on the light or shadow box. You are now ready to block out the screen.

CHAPTER VI

BLOCKING OR STOPPING OUT THE SCREEN

R ED sable or lettering quill brushes are best for blocking out. There are two different ways of filling in the screen, one for a "cut-in" job, in which the background is to be screened, and the other in which the lettering is to be screened, as is the job we now have in

Figure 29.—Screen for First Color.

hand. Various solutions can be used for blocking and they have various trade names, but are mostly known as stencil filler, sealer lacquo, etc. They are all of the same base, namely, nitrocellulose lacquer. Some will flow easier and better, and only experimenting will prove

RED PLATE

Figure 30.—Screen for Second Color.

which is the best suited to your individual use and taste. A thinner is also used to make the solution work easier and also to wash the screen out when the job is run. While blocking out, this thinner is used the same as turps in painting with oil or japan colors. It may be purchased or can be made with the following formula:

1 gal. amyl-acetate
1 gal. acetone
½ gal. benzol or solvent naphtha

While working with the sealer, use a single straight stroke, as any attempt to go over the same place will result in pulling up the sealer and will also cause pinholes. Your screen for your first color after being properly blocked out will look like Fig. 29.

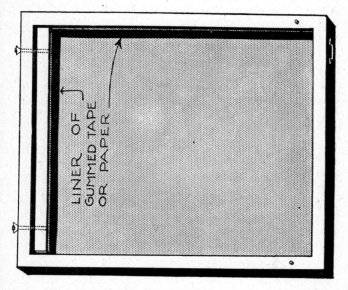

LINER OF GUMMED TAPE OR PAPER

Figure 31.—Inside Edge of Frame Showing Tape.

In the early practice of screen work, one color was piled on top of another. This present improved method consists of making the entire screen and blocking out the portions not desired for the first color with a water filler which is easily washed out with water. It is not harmed by gasoline, naphtha or even the lacquer thinner. On this job we will run red first. As we will not want the red color to go through the open portions of the screen that are intended for blue and green, we will block out these letters and the green border with the water filler. When this is done your screen will look like Fig. 30.

To prevent the paint from leaking through along the inside edge of the frame, gummed tape about 2 inches wide is placed on the inside of the frame, as shown in Fig. 31. Also place gummed tape on the bottom of the screen. You are now ready to run the job.

CHAPTER VII

RUNNING THE JOB

E FFICIENCY is as important in screen work as in
any other line. Speed in running cuts the cost.
Proper equipment must be used properly. To obtain the
best results equipment should be arranged so that it is
handy to use and for easy disposition of the finished card.
The best way to arrange equipment is shown in Fig. 32.
Paper or cardboard is placed to the right of the unit
which should be on the center of the table; paint and all
other sundries, such as varnishes, paint rags, etc., should
be placed to the left. The drying rack should be directly
in the rear so that cards can be placed in it without unnecessary steps. In Chapter III, "Paints Used in Screen
Work," will be found complete data as to varieties,
strength, etc., of paints.

Place a sheet of blank cardboard beneath the frame and
against the markers and lower frame. Then place about
a pint of paint on the inside of frame and with the squeegee roll this over the screen; only ordinary pressure is
necessary. This action forces the paint through the
open meshes of the screen, thereby producing the display.
The first two or three copies will not be perfect, as the
silk absorbs a certain amount of the oils in the paint and
it requires several impressions to right this.

After completing the run of red, clean the screen well
with a mixture of kerosene and gasoline. When clean,

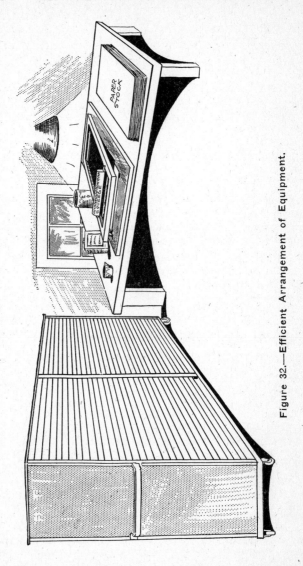

Figure 32.—Efficient Arrangement of Equipment.

wash out the water filler with water, being sure that no filler remains in the meshes of the silk and then rewash with kerosene and gasoline in order to remove any paint that may still remain. Your screen will now be in its original state with only the lacquer-filled screen remaining. You are now ready for the next color, which is blue. Proceed as before, blocking the red and green portion with the water filler; then run the blue. Repeat this same operation for the last color, green.

The job, now completed, is ready for delivery. Care must be taken not to pile the cards one on top of another before they are completely dry as the entire job is ruined if they stick. It should be remembered that paper has a tendency to generate a certain amount of heat especially if piled in any quantity. If the paint is the least bit tacky this heat is certain to soften the paint, resulting in sticking, and when unpacking and pulling them apart, the sticky paint will pull the paper from the card above it. Wax paper may be placed between each card, but this is an added expense and is unnecessary if the cards are handled properly.

CHAPTER VIII

ESTIMATING THE JOB

TOO much stress cannot be placed on the importance of every processor keeping close and accurate records of the cost of each job. It is not enough that he keep a haphazard record of the paint, cardboard, silk cost and other materials that run into volume. If the shop is to stay in business and make a reasonable margin of profit on every job turned out, it is absolutely essential that accurate cost be kept on every item that enters into the production of every process job. This should by all means include overhead charges, cost of selling, commissions paid, in fact, every expense incurred by the processor in the conduct of his business. If it is a small shop in which the proprietor sells his own jobs, and then comes back to the shop and by himself or with the help of one or two assistants turns out the job, he has incurred selling cost just as definitely as he would if he were employing a salesman. Every minute of time that is actually spent on the job must be computed in figuring cost.

A great deal of emphasis may be placed upon the subject of cost and prices in selling every process job at a fair price. By fair price is meant a price at which the job is sold at a reasonable margin of profit. Price cutting is a practice that should not be indulged in by any processor who intends to remain in business for any length of time. While such tactics may secure a few small jobs that would not have been secured otherwise, it will lead eventually to lost business and lack of confidence in the shop by the purchasers of process signs and displays.

It is far better to turn out one job at a fair margin of profit than two jobs which are sold practically at cost.

An estimate on the three-color lettering job, as shown in Fig. 27, which we have described, will be found in the table below:

1,000 sheets 8-ply cardboard	$70.00
1 yard 13XX stencil silk	7.00
Screen labor, 8 hrs. @ $2 hr	16.00
1 gal. red paint	5.00
1 gal. green paint	4.00
Running labor, 18 hrs. @ $1 hr	18.00
Misc. as sealer tape, cleaner, etc.	2.00
1 gal. blue paint	5.00
Art work	10.00
Racking, packing, one man, 4 hrs. @ $1 hr.	4.00
	$141.00
Overhead 30%	42.30
	$183.30

To this is added the salesman's commission, which is ordinarily 20%, also profit, which should not be judged by the cost of production but by the value of the article.

CHAPTER IX

"TROUBLE SHOOTING" WHILE SCREENING

I HAVE purposely omitted mentioning some of the pitfalls and troubles that are apt to be encountered so as not to confuse or distract from the main points in the description of building of the equipment and the running of the job.

In the following paragraphs I will endeavor to clear up some of the seemingly perplexing troubles that may arise.

SCREEN CLOGGING

Although screen clogging will seem to be one of the worst stumbling blocks to the beginner, it is easy to avoid if the following suggestions are heeded. Improperly ground paints are the source of most of this difficulty. The paint made for process work seldom gives trouble as it is ground especially fine to go through the finest mesh silk; it also has properties for the prevention of paint hardening in the screen. On certain surfaces, such as cardboard, a variation will be found as to the absorbent qualities, some boards absorbing the liquids in the paint so rapidly that the pigment (that is, the color) cannot go through the screen, but sticks to the meshes of the silk. If the screen clogs in this manner wash it off, top and bottom, with a mixture of one-third kerosene and two-thirds gasoline or benzine. The paint that is in the unit should be placed back into the paint pail and to this then add about three tablespoons of litho No. 3 varnish or "No Clog" to the quart. A little kerosene may also be added, but sparingly, as kerosene if used too heavily will leave an oil mark on a cardboard surface.

Another cause of clogging is lint or edges of paper which are present after being cut. These will stick to the bottom of the screen and will gather paint pigment, causing a spot. Each sheet before being placed beneath the screen should be wiped or shaken to be sure that lint is not present.

Still another cause of clogging is improper pressure on the squeegee when running; usually not heavy enough pressure. The base may even cause clogging if there are low spots in it. The squeegee running over the base will print on the highest portions of the base only. Clogging may occur if the screen had been used before and is not properly cleaned out. If the equipment is in good order and special process paints are used, clogging will not cause trouble.

CHAPTER X

THE SINGLE SCREEN OR ELIMINATION PROCESS

FIGURE 33 shows a copy of seven colors to be reproduced with a single screen; one color is placed on top of another, eliminating the last one on the screen as it is finished. In a job having a large number of colors there will be an embossed appearance and in this case a wonderful effect is produced, the letters or illustrations standing out in relief from the background. It is hard to set a definite rule as to what color to run first, or which color is to be the background, as all jobs vary.

A good policy is to take the largest surface of color, providing it is not of a lake base, and use this as the background color. On this run, it will be noted, however, that the largest open portion is black, therefore, the background color will be black. It is advisable to coat the background on a coating machine, but if this is impossible, it may be screened through a coarse mesh silk.

As white screens perfectly over black and gives a good base for our future colors, the first screening will be white. Fig. 34 shows the screen prepared for the run of white. It will be noted that everything is run white except that portion which is to remain black. Run the white and when finished, clean the screen with the gasoline mixture, being sure the meshes are well cleaned. You

Figure 33.—Copy for Screen Using Seven Colors, One on Top of Another.

Figure 34.—Screen Ready for the Run of White.

Figure 35.—Screen Ready for the Run of Blue.

are now ready to eliminate, on the screen, those portions that are to remain white. Place your master copy on the base and on the screen mark out those portions that are to remain white. Block this out with blocking-out solution. The screen will now look like Fig. 35. Through this screen run the blue. After the blue has been run,

Figure 36.—Screen Ready for the Run of Yellow.

eliminate those portions that are to remain blue. After this has been done the screen will now look like Fig. 36. The next color to run is the yellow. It is not advisable to run too often portions of the design that have any great amount of detail, and as the package has much lettering, it is best to eliminate it as soon as possible; therefore, the yellow is run next. Now eliminate those portions that are to remain yellow and the screen will look like Fig. 37. The next color to run is light gray. When

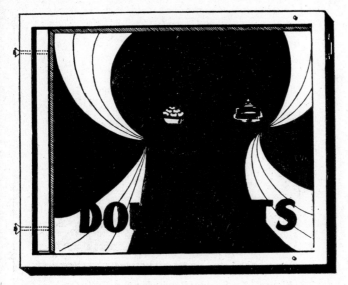

Figure 37.—Screen Ready for the Run of Light Gray.

this is screened, eliminate the light gray and the screen will appear as in Fig. 38. The next color is medium gray. When this is screened, eliminate it and the screen will now appear as in Fig. 39. Next run the dark gray. After eliminating this, the screen will appear as in Fig. 40, which is for the brown, the last color. The job is now completed.

Cost on above run:

```
1,000 sheets black matt board @ 7¢....$ 70.00
2 gal. white process paint @ $4........    8.00
1½ gal. blue @ $5..................         7.50
1 gal. yellow @ $5..................        5.00
½ gal. gray @ $4..................          2.00
½ gal. gray @ $4..................          2.00
½ gal gray @ $4..................           2.00
```

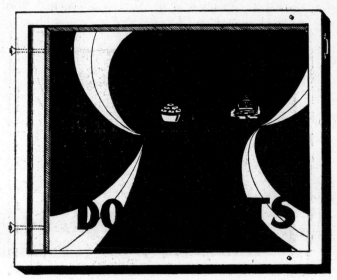

Figure 38.—Screen Ready for the Dark Gray.

1 quart brown @ $4................	1.00
Screen labor, 18 hrs. @ $2 per hr....	36.00
Running and racking, 2 men, 49 hrs. @ $1 hr.........................	98.00
Misc.	10.00
Packing, etc......................	5.00
Original drawing..................	25.00
	$271.50
Overhead 30%....................	81.45
	$352.95
Profit 50%.......................	176.47
	$529.42
Sales Commission 20%.............	105.88
Selling price.....................	$635.30

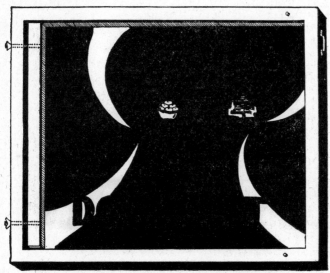

Figure 39.—Screen Ready for the Medium Gray.

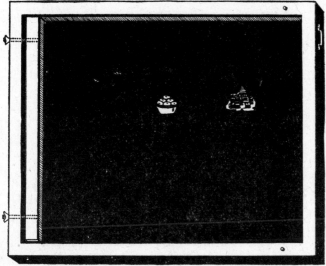

Figure 40.—Screen Ready for the Brown.

CHAPTER XI

PAPER MASK STENCIL

FOR any job in which the size of the lettering is fairly large and the quantity small, the paper cut-out stencil is best. The advantageous point is the speed with which the stencil can be made and handled. The best paper is draughtsman's tracing paper (not the waxed variety). This is first laid over the copy and traced. Fig. 41 is an example of a sign to be screened. The background is white, the letters black.

Cut out the letters, and in those like O, A, B, P, etc., where there are centers, number the centers as well as the paper mask. See Fig. 41. This is done so that the right centers may be placed in the correct places, because when they are cut out, they all look alike and it is easy to place the centers in the wrong places and thus spoil the letters. After the mask has been cut out, lay the original on the base and on this lay the paper mask. Place the centers in their respective places; lower the blank screen, place paint on the screen and with a squeegee screen this and the paint will hold the paper to the screen. The paint must be of the correct consistency as it is impossible to clean this type of screen without removing the paper mask. This method will prove a time-saver in runs of from 5 to 50. The mask can be removed, cleaned and filed away for further use.

For larger quantities the following method will prove

Figure 41.—A Paper Cut-Out Stencil.

better. Trace the copy on the stenciled paper and give this a coat of shellac. Allow this to dry and with a stencil knife cut out as instructed in a previous chapter. For a cutting base use a sheet of glass or zinc beneath the paper while cutting. Lay this on a flat table that has been padded with several sheets of newspaper. Be sure that there are no wrinkles and that the paper lies absolutely level, then on this place the screen, the shellaced side towards the screen. On the inside of the screen lay a piece of newspaper and with a warm flatiron (not hot) iron on the newspaper. This will soften the shellac and it will adhere to the screen. The centers are attached in the same way. Be sure to shellac one side of the paper only and that the side with the tracing on it. Sheet celluloid can be used the same way, attaching the celluloid to the screen with celluloid cement.

CHAPTER XII

THE SINGLE STENCIL METHOD OF REPRODUCTION

THE safest way to reproduce a multicolor job with the silk screen method is to use a separate screen for each color. It is a longer process because separate screens or a series of screens must be made for each color, but it has its advantages, as perfect register can be obtained and also a minimum amount of paint is used.

Fig. 42 is a four-color job on white stock, size 22 by 28 inches. To start we will use a white background or white stock. As black carries all the detail work, this will have to be put on top, that is, it will be one of the last colors to be run.

As yellow is an under color that will not interfere with the detail color, we will run this color first. After preparing the frame and screen in the usual manner, proceed to mark on the silk the portions that are to remain yellow. It is good practice to extend just a hair line on the outside of the copy so as not to produce any white or background spots; the black outline to be run later will cover this. The first screen prepared for the run of yellow should look like Fig. 43.

After the yellow is run, the screen is entirely cleaned out and prepared for the next color, green. It will be seen that the green is also an under color and that the black outline will overlap and cover this. The green is marked out on the screen and blocked out and should appear as in Fig. 44. It should be remembered that the

Figure 42.—Copy for a Four-Color Job.

YELLOW
Figure 43.—Screen Prepared for Run of Yellow.

GREEN
Figure 44.—Screen Prepared for Run of Green.

master sketch, or original, is placed beneath this screen for tracing each color.

The next color to be run is black. The red does not interfere with the black, so it is left until last. The black screen is the hardest to produce as it has all the detail work on it. It can now be seen how the black will overlap the yellow and green. It is a good idea to place one of the copies with the yellow and green colors run on it beneath the screen to test the markings that have been made and see if they are correct and cover these colors.

The screen for the black will look like Fig. 45. The red screen has very little on it, and when done, will look like Fig. 46.

BLACK

Figure 45.—Screen for the Black.

Figure 46.—Screen for the Red.

CHAPTER XIII

THE PHOTOGRAPHIC OR SENSITIZED SCREEN

FOR reproducing small detail work and perfect lettering on small jobs of process work the sensitized screen is the only method that can be utilized. Newspaper type of small size can be very satisfactorily reproduced if the screen is properly made. The method of getting the copy on the sensitized screen is somewhat similar to photographic methods. The copy corresponds to a photographic negative, therefore the design or lettering must be drawn on paper transparent enough for light to penetrate it.

The screen is coated with a sensitizing solution that hardens when exposed to the light.

The copy (on transparent paper) is placed on the sensitized screen and put under strong light. The letters or design in the copy are opaque, the light only hardens the background. After exposure to light the screen is held under running water, and the unhardened portions (that is, the letters) are washed away, thus leaving the background intact. (There is an article on the market that requires only heating in water, but several formulas that will work satisfactorily are given below.)

This method of making screens requires more experimenting and effort than any other screen method, as climatic conditions will play quite a part in its success or failure. To start with, a room of even temperature is necessary, as dampness will not allow the solution to set properly. Also a dark room is necessary in which to make the plates before they are exposed.

The following formula for a sensitizing solution is, in my opinion, the best: Dissolve ¾ oz. (avoirdupois) pulverized bichromate of ammonium in 4 oz. (liquid measure) warm distilled water. Pour this into a special brown or blue bottle and let stand for about an hour. Put 1 oz. (avoirdupois) Nazdar photo glue * in 8 oz. of cold water. Let this stand or soak for about an hour. Pour the first solution into the glue solution, adding 2 oz. (avoirdupois) warm Le Page's photo-engravers' glue. Place this mixture into a double boiler, add 10 drops of glycerine, stir the mixture well. Put water in the outer boiler and heat to the boiling point, then place the inner boiler in this and boil the water until the solution is hot. Do not allow the solution itself to come to a boil. Strain several times and take this solution into the dark room. Hereafter all work must be done in the dark room until the screen has been exposed. The mesh is fastened to the screen in the regular way. Silk mesh of about 16XX is used. While the solution is still hot, brush it on the screen with a 2-inch brush, either camel-hair or badger. Use long strokes and avoid going over the same surface twice as it will pull up. Lay the screen flat and allow it to dry. When entirely dry, coat the opposite side, stroking in the opposite direction. As before mentioned, this must be done in the dark room. A red or ruby light must be used. This solution will be colorless on the screen and it is hard to detect pinholes or register properly. To overcome this, dye or color may be used. This is made as follows: Dissolve ½ oz. (avoirdupois) water soluble purple analine dye in ½ oz.

* NOTE. It is not the intention of the author to favor any certain firm or product, but in cases where they are mentioned, it is the only item of its kind that may be used for that particular purpose.

denatured alcohol. This sets up a rapid solution. Add dye and alcohol to 8 oz. water and stir thoroughly. Use 2 oz. of this dye solution instead of 2 oz. of water in making the sensitized solution. Dye solution should be added to the glue solution before boiling.

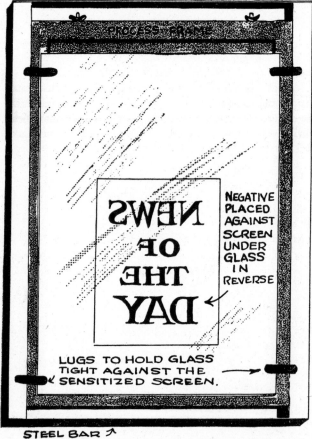

Figure 47.—Outer Frame for Sensitized Screen.

After the screen is dry, it is ready for printing (that is, exposure to light through the transparent paper copy). A printing frame is necessary and Fig. 47 shows the printing frame with the process frame in position inside of it. The printing frame is made of lumber the same thickness as the process frame with four clamps on each side, one side to hold the glass in position, the other to hold a backing pad tight against the screen. It will be noted in Fig. 47 that the sensitized screen is in place with the copy against it and on the copy a glass is fastened to hold it tight against the screen. The copy should be made

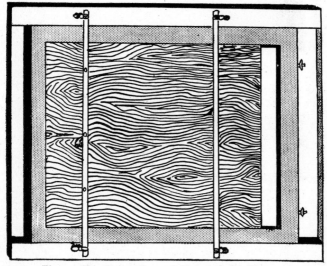

Figure 48.—Rear View of Frame with Braces.

on a thin transparent paper. If care is taken, the copy can sometimes be attached to the sensitized screen with axle grease and thus eliminate the use of the printing frame. Coat the paper on the inked side with the grease, rubbing out with a piece of cardboard. This will tend to take out the wrinkles and air bubbles, leaving the copy tight against the screen.

Fig. 48 shows the rear of the printing frame with the padded board and braces in place. These will hold the screen tight against the copy and the glass, preventing light from getting under and between copy and screen.

Assuming that the copy is in place against the screen and the padded block, we are ready to expose it. On a bright day only 30 minutes are necessary, but on a dark, cloudy day from 4 to 6 hours are required. A good arc or flood light can be used and will eliminate all the guess-work in exposing. Over-exposure is almost impossible, but if a screen is exposed for too long a time before washing, it will commence to crystallize. Pinholes will then be the result. These also are caused by an improper solution, a bad batch of glue or from grime and soot settling onto the screen before it is dry. Touching the screen while it is still wet will cause pinholes.

A good way to tell if the screen has been exposed enough is to lift up a little corner of the copy. If sufficiently exposed the background will bear a burnt appearance against the copy which will remain in its natural color. If it has been exposed enough hold the screen under running water, washing by shaking back and forth. Do not touch it with the hands, rag or brush. A hose will remove the solution nicely. *Never* touch the screen while it is wet. After you are sure that you have it well cleaned, set it up to dry.

The screen is now ready to run. In case several colors are to be run and certain portions of the screen are to be blocked out, this may be done with lacquer filler and removed with the acetone solution, as these will not harm the screen. Any fillers having glycerine, glue or syrups will be apt to crystallize the screen, resulting in pinholes.

If a large quantity is to be run, here is a plan for making a screen to print two, four, six or more at one time.

Take the original design and make a small sensitized screen of this one. Run as many copies as you need on a thin transparent paper and mount as many as you need on whatever size screen you care to sensitize, and expose them all at one time.

To process a halftone, which is a photo or picture made with dots, you can obtain from any photo or engraving houses the regular halftone negatives and place these against your sensitized screen, as you would an ordinary copy, then expose as you would any other job. Never try to run any finer than a 60-line halftone screen as the dots will be blurry. These halftone negatives can be made, but require special equipment, such as cameras, lights, etc. Therefore it is best for the process man to have his negatives and positives made by a photo engraver unless he knows enough about the photographic process to insure success. As a rule this type of screen will not hold up as long as the handmade lacquer screen, but by "treating" it, it can be made to stand up under ordinary usage for some time. This treating can be accomplished by coating the entire screen on one side with the lacquer filler and before it is entirely hard, wash out on the opposite side with the lacquer thinners. It will require tactful handling.

To reproduce type matter, have a printer pull several proofs on a thin transparent paper with a heavy black ink, and while the ink is still wet, dust it with an aluminum or gold bronze. This will make it opaque and light proof. Do not use letters with small spurs, and when placing the copy against the screen for baking, have it on a slight angle or slant so that the sides and tops of the letters will not run on an even angle with the threads of silk, as this will cause ragged edges.

To remove the sensitizing solution from screens, take one part lye to eight parts water and with a stick and rag "swab-wash" well with the mixture. It is advisable to let the lye solution soak for about ten minutes in order to soften the screen coating. A scrub brush may then be used with warm water. The screen must be perfectly clean for sensitizing.

Another sensitizing solution is given below:

Mixture "A"—Have a druggist weigh on apothecary's scale 260 grains of bicarbonate potassium and 70 grains bichromate ammonium. Dissolve in 10 oz. of hot distilled water.

Mixture "B"—Mix 12 oz. Le Page's photo-engravers' glue in 8 oz. hot distilled water.

Mixture "C"—Mix the whites of 3 fresh eggs in 4 oz. warm distilled water.

Add "A" and "B" together; when cold, add "C." Stir in 6 grains chromic acid, 25 drops of ammonia water (28 per cent solution), 20 drops glycerine, and strain this mixture through a double cheesecloth into a dark-colored bottle. This solution is not brushed on to the screen but is flowed on, being sure that the screen is well covered. A drip pan is placed beneath the screen to receive the flow because this draining can be placed back into the bottle and used again.

CHAPTER XIV

THE PAINT PRESS METHOD OF REPRODUCTION

THE paint press is by no means new but it has been adopted by the process industry. Lithographers used it years ago to reproduce large metal signs. It is a most reliable method when making large metal or paper signs, and has been used almost exclusively to reproduce window backgrounds. The paint can be used with a heavier varnish and japan body, making it ideal for outdoor displays, especially when they are exposed to the sun. The process consists in placing a gelatine blanket, on which is the design, on a large cylinder and by running this surface over a paint slab, picking up the paint and transferring it onto the metal, card, etc.

Fig. 49 shows the construction of the paint press with the paint "pickup slab." Fig. 50 shows the more modern press with automatic paint distributing rollers, etc. It is an investment of considerable size but the initial cost is practically the last, as all further expenses are small. The wheels that run on the track are of the railroad type and are standard equipment, as are the bearing boxes which can be easily purchased. The wooden cylinder must be absolutely true and smooth to insure good work. A steel cable is fastened to one end of the table and wound around the cylinder or drum six times, then fastened to the other end. Turnbuckles are fastened to the cable, then to the cable hooks, which are on the ends of the table. These are used to keep the cable tight, as a loose cable will allow the cylinder to shift, resulting in the

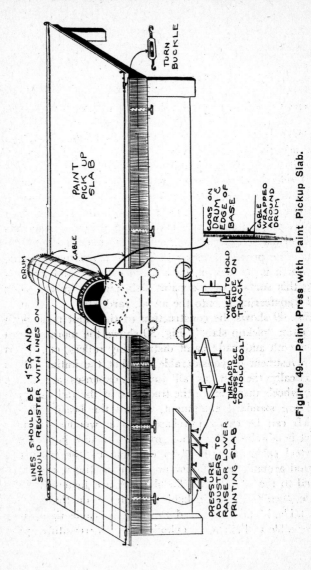

Figure 49.—Paint Press with Paint Pickup Slab.

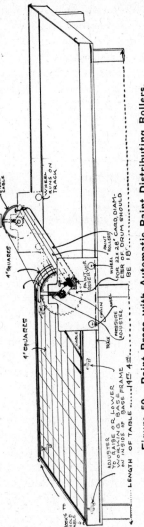

Figure 50.—Paint Press with Automatic Paint Distributing Rollers.

copy being off center or register. This cable is on each end of the cylinder. The working base must be level and should be made of metal or hard wood. The gear driving the distributing rollers should have a catch-peg to stop the roller from revolving when the cylinder is run in reverse or to the printing position. This will prevent the rollers from spreading a heavy layer of paint on the cylinder which would result in a smeary letter or outline. The composition paint distributing rollers are 3 inches wide and can be purchased in any printer's supply house. If using the press in Fig. 49, these rollers are unnecessary as the drum is rolled over a slab upon which the paint has been spread, the drum picking up the paint from the slab.

Take the original sketch and on this mark 4-inch squares. If the unit or cylinder is very large, add ½ inch to the foot on the sketch to allow for shrinkage of the gelatine. Four-inch squares are also marked off on the cylinder as well as on the printing base. Register is obtained through these squares. On a piece of thin tracing paper, copy the design including the squares. An H B pencil should be used. Place ordinary linseed oil putty in a large vessel and bake on a stove, keeping the putty in motion to prevent burning. Bake until the oil is out, which will be about 12 hours and possibly 15 to 20 hours. While still on the fire, add raw linseed oil until the putty becomes rubbery or like a heavy paste. This putty must be heated each time before using. For efficient work, a large table with a carbonized steel top is best. This is to be used for laying the putty mold and cutting and therefore a flat smooth base that will not scratch is almost necessary. The large table will be found to be advantageous as several jobs or several colors for the same run can be laid out and made at the same time.

On this base spread the putty to a thickness of $\frac{3}{32}$ inch. Roll it out as level as possible. If the putty is dry or brittle, take a little raw linseed oil on the hands and rub over the putty, being careful not to wet too much. On this putty surface now place the tracing, "pencil side" against the putty, and with a 5-inch putty-knife, rub over the tracing, thus transferring the pencil design to the putty. For the 4-inch squares use a perforating wheel, perforating through onto the putty. These marks on the finished blanket will register with the similar squares that are on the cylinder.

Take a good steel stencil knife blade and sharpen up about an inch on both sides. Place this in a blade holder. If the design has not been completely transferred, roll with a felt roller. In the case of a sign with a cut-out background, where the letters are to be printed, the letters are cut out on the putty, and where the background is to be printed, the background is cut away on the putty. The cutting in the putty is done with a stencil knife, being sure to cut down to the steel base using a good sharp cut, eliminating short jerky cuts, as these will leave ragged edges. When it has been cut and the putty removed from the portions that are to be printed, take a fly sprayer or a small brush and either paint or spray onto the steel base where the putty has been removed a very thin layer of raw linseed oil. This prevents the gelatine from sticking to the table or sides of the putty. The mold is now ready for pouring the gelatine solution.

The gelatine solution is made as follows: Use two vessels or boilers, one a trifle larger than the other, making a double boiler. The inner one should be of at least 3-gallon capacity. Place 1½ gal. of glycerine, which has been heated to a boiling point, in this inner vessel. In a separate vessel heat 1 gallon of high-test glue; pour this into the inner boiler with the hot glycerine, stirring thoroughly until it is well dissolved. Cool for about 30 minutes and pour this solution onto the putty mold, first filling the letters by using a dipper or cup. If the solution is poured directly from the large container, the letters are more apt to become rounded or damaged. A flat steel bar has been placed around the mold to prevent the composition from running over the sides. This should be ¼ inch higher than the top of the putty. Pour the gelatine composition so that it will come flush with the top of these bars, letting it set for 12 hours. A piece of canvas is cut a trifle larger than the mold and with a warm iron is ironed onto the composition form. When the canvas has adhered securely, pull the composition from the table and the putty mold. Lay this blanket back onto the table and cut out small squares or circles on the blanket where it will do no damage to the copy, this to enable you to register the squares which show from the perforations on the blanket with the similar squares on the cylinder. Fasten this blanket to the cylinder with tacks, matching the squares on the blanket with the squares on the cylinder. A good method to get perfect register is to place the original on the base, fastening markers around it on the base. Then lay the composition blanket on this, face down, matching the letters or design. Roll the cylinder over onto this and fasten.

Put the paint in the paint reservoir and run back and forth several times to distribute the paint evenly. The blank sign is then laid in place against the marker and the cylinder rolled over this, thereby making a print. After the gelatine blanket is no longer needed it can be melted and used again. The putty should always be kept in an air-tight can and covered with a thin layer of oil. Japan paint is best suited for this purpose and should be procured from a house that makes paint exclusively for this line of business.

If using the press, Fig. 49, the paint is placed on the rear slab and the cylinder run over this each time, thus picking up its paint supply. If only a portion of the sign prints, the pressure adjusters should be changed as these will either raise or lower the base.

CHAPTER XV

PAPER SIGNS, LITHOGRAPHIC IMPRINTS, ETC.

MANY process men avoid jobs to be run on paper because they fear there is much trouble and little profit in this sort of work. On the other hand, others have found a profitable field in the small quantity runs of paper—window signs, streamers, notices, manugraphs or imprints.

Lithographers have long sought to produce satisfactory imprints on their 24-sheet and other large posters other than printing. It can readily be seen that the cost of setting up type, make-ready, presswork, etc., for a quantity of 3 to 5 or 6 is much too great. Furthermore, printing does not match the lithography.

By imprint or manugraph is meant the placing of a local dealer's name on a lithographed poster of a nationally advertised product.

The posters themselves are printed in large quantities, for example, 250,000 of one for a well-known tire. This tire is handled by 20,000 dealers, thus making 20,000 different imprints and only 3 to 100 posters for each imprint of a dealer's name. These dealer imprints in quantities of over three can be processed at a profit and at less cost than printing.

Furthermore, the process work will be far better than printing, with an individual appearance not obtainable with type. I have myself made 50 changes in an hour, running 3 to 5 of each on work of this kind.

[93]

Fig. 51 shows a billboard with an imprint. The method used for this work is by means of the paper screen. As names vary in number of letters and as the space is always the same, different widths and types of letters are necessary. These are made on cardboard, cut and shellacked. About fifteen various types will be plenty.

Figure 51.—Billboard with Imprint.

The paper for the imprints is laid on a flat base, the letters arranged in place and traced around with a pencil. These are then cut out with a stencil knife, markers being placed on the base. One of the blank sheets for imprinting is placed in position against the markers. On this lay the cut-out in its own place, lower the screen and with the squeegee, run the paint over the screen. This will not only print the first copy, but will fasten the cut-out pattern to the screen. Run the amount desired and pull off the cut-out pattern, repeating this with the next copy. It can readily be seen that a vast quantity can be made per hour. Short-run one-, two- and even three-sheet posters can be processed. The author is very well acquainted with a plant now turning out 24-sheet posters complete with the silk screen method. Sale or window streamers can also be made profitably by using a short-

Figure 52.—Frame with Bridge.

cut method of running several colors with one "swipe"
of the squeegee.

For example, suppose that an order is received for 500
each of three varieties of streamers in two colors, the
price in red and the wording in blue. The three designs
are made on the same plate, as the average streamer is
7 by 24 or 28 inches. The frame will easily handle
these three, but in making the sketch allow about two
inches between the item and the price as a bridge will be
placed in this space. Fig. 52. The stencil is made with
the cut-out paper screen or the regular lacquer-filled
screen. The bridge is made by cutting a piece of cardboard the height of the frame and two inches wide. Two
pieces of gummed tape are fastened half to the cardboard
and half to the screen. See Fig. 53. The gummed tape is

placed on both sides of the cardboard. The purpose of this is to keep the two colors apart while running. Next, two squeegees are cut to fit the widths of the colors and fastened together (as in Fig. 54) by iron bands screwed

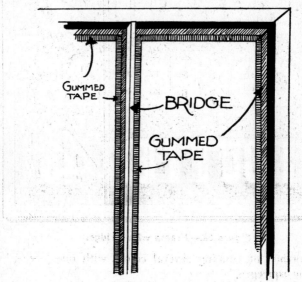

Figure 53.—Bridge Fastened with Tape.

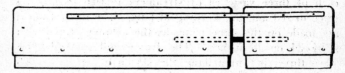

Figure 54.—Squeegee for Running Two Colors at Once.

on each side of the squeegee. Thus, by one "swipe" of the squeegee both the red and the blue are run. A special paper process paint should be used for such work as it dries almost immediately, permitting the sheets to be cut in an hour.

CHAPTER XVI

PROCESSING TYPEWRITTEN LETTERS AND DRAWINGS

THIS is one of the most recent improvements in process work, and if properly developed, will open a field that heretofore has not been touched, namely, the reproducing of typewritten letters with original signatures. Fig. 55 is a copy done through a screen, black on white stock. Fig. 56 is on blue stock with gold paint. In Fig. 57 is shown the processing of testimonial letters at

PIGGLY WIGGLY INC. June 23rd, 1930
NATIONAL TEA CO.

     C O R R E C T I O N S

QUEEN OLIVES on page 2 of Bulletin
No. 34.

Item reads "10# Queen Olives" -
Should be "10c Queen Olives"

Under Price Changes - Reads "National Olives 16 oz. at 49c" - this
should be 40c

Figure 55.—Typewritten Copy, Black on White Stock.

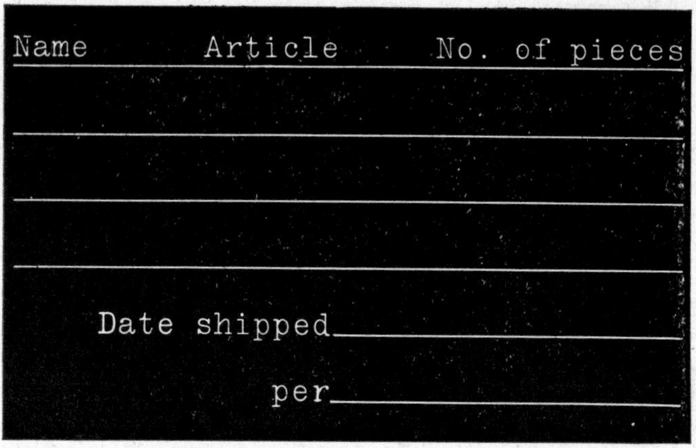

Name	Article	No. of pieces

Date shipped_____

per_____

Figure 56.—Typewritten Copy, Gold Paint on Blue Stock.

Figure 57.—Processing Testimonial Letters.

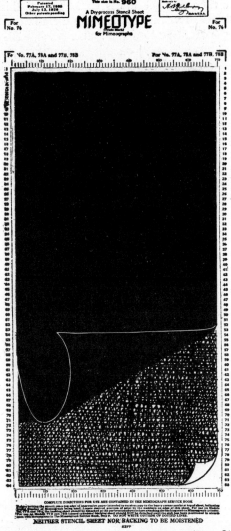

Figure 58.—Vellum Paper Used in Typewritten Stencils.

the same time that the job is run. To use this method, obtain sheets of vellum paper from a stationer. Fig. 58. This is the kind used on the mimeograph. Also get the two special pencils used on this particular paper. These are to reproduce signatures and line drawings.

The screen is made the same as for any other job except where the testimonial letters are placed. These spaces are left open to receive the sheets of vellum paper. Now, on a typewriter cut the stencil, and where the signature is to appear, write it with a special pencil. Tear off the blue sheet, lay it in position, and with one swipe of the squeegee and paint, this sheet will stick to the screen. If running only the letters or the vellum stencil with a line drawing, simply fasten these without any other copy. These stencils are not advisable for long runs, but it is a simple matter to make a fresh vellum stencil and mount

CHAPTER XVII

HOW TO MAKE STICK-ON LETTERS

THE method of making gold leaf letters in the shop and pasting or fastening them to a window is old, but very few sign men have taken advantage of this method, possibly because of lack of knowledge in making them. There are times when a merchant will not care to pay for a hand-lettered gold leaf sign, but would use a stick-on letter sign.

There are various types of letters used. The commonest type used is the plain gold leaf letter without shade or outline. To make this, take a sheet of thin tin foil and on this coat a layer of fat oil gold size, thinning the gold size to meet requirements as to drying. When tacky or almost dry, gild with gold leaf. If a high-class job is desired, use a good grade of gold leaf, but when price

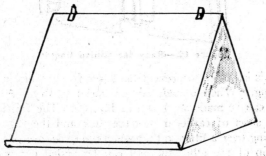

Figure 59.—A Handy Gilding Device.

is the important factor use the cheaper grade with an aluminum back. When gilded, burnish with a wad of cotton batting until it has a bright gloss, being careful not to rub too hard. A good device can be made to make gilding easier by taking a board set on an angle with a side piece. The tin foil is clamped to the top with the clothespin type clamp. A small tray on the bottom catches the gold leaf that drops and this should be saved as it can be resold, as can the tin foil. Fig. 59. In the case of a quantity job, coat about 25 sheets. When these are done give each sheet a coat of the following solution:

> 1 part clear Egyptian lacquer
> 2 parts lacquer thinner

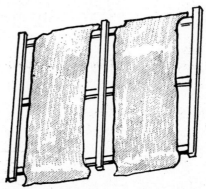

Figure 60.—Rack for Gilded Sheets.

This is put on to prevent the letter from tarnishing and peeling. When coated, lay on racks to dry. A good rack can be made as shown in Fig. 60. The foil is laid on a sheet of cardboard on the rack and the edges left hanging over a little so that when the racks are piled one on top of the other the foil can be pulled out without taking down the entire stack of racks. When dry, take 25 sheets and lay them one on top of the other in a box-

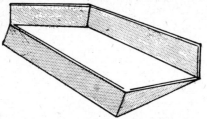

Figure 61.—Box for Dry Gilded Sheets.

like arrangement. See Fig. 61. This will keep them all
even as the foil cannot easily be jogged to an even edge.
If it is intended to standardize on any type of letter, a
complete alphabet is cut out of cardboard. Take the foil
and lay it on a steel sheet or a piece of glass. On these
25 sheets lay the letter that is to be cut out and with a
good sharp stencil knife cut around the pattern letter.

Figure 62.—A Shaded Letter.

Twenty-five letters will thus be cut with one operation.
Repeat this for each letter. This completes the plain
letter.

A plain letter is seldom sold, the shaded or outline
letter being the type most frequently used. A separate
pattern is needed for this and it can be made from the
plain letter by laying this letter on a sheet of cardboard
(sixteen ply being best for all these patterns) which
should be shellaced to preserve them. First draw the

shade and then cut out the letter, as in Fig. 62. If the letter is to have a black shade or outline, take the sheet tin foil and with a soft brush coat it black with the following solution:

> 1 lb. lettering black in oil
> 2 lbs. sp. drop black in japan
> 2 oz. quick rubbing varnish
> Thin only with turpentine.

When this is dry, cut out letters as previously done with the plain letter. Fasten the plain gold letter onto the black shade letter with the following solution:

> 1 part quick rubbing varnish
> 5 parts japan drier
> 10 parts turpentine.

In fastening, do not cover entire black letter or back of plain letter, but dab several spots on back of plain gold letter.

Other colors for outlines or shades are listed below and it is an important matter to follow these formulas as a surplus of one ingredient is apt to result in cracking or chipping:

> Red—1 lb. English vermilion (deep) in oil
> 1 lb. permanent red japan
> 3 oz. quick rubbing varnish. Thin with turps
> Blue—1 lb. cobalt blue in oil
> 1 lb. super cobalt blue in japan
> ¼ lb. ultramarine blue in oil
> 3 oz. quick rubbing varnish. Thin with turps
> Green—1 lb. chrome green light in oil
> ½ lb. chrome green in japan
> 2 oz. quick rubbing varnish. Thin with turps.

Outline letters are made the same as shade letters.

To make a script sign first draw your copy, then take a sheet of thin paper a little larger than your sign and lay it on a table. On this lay the tin foil, the gold side up, and coat with coating "dope." When quite dry lay the copy over this and trace with a sharp pencil, using just enough pressure so that it can be seen on the foil. Cut out the entire job, and when this is finished, lay a sheet of paper on it. In the case of an outline or a shade, lay the cut-out plain letters on the colored foil and cut out as wanted. The sheets on the top and bottom are

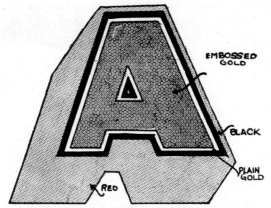

Figure 63.—Embossed Letter with Gold and Black Outlines and a Red Shade.

to keep it smooth and even and when taking it to the job it is an easy matter to unroll it. When ready to put up, unroll and take sheet off of the top and coat letters with equal parts of spar varnish and gasoline, then with a helper taking an end of the paper, place it into position, rolling with a roller or pad; then take off the paper. The back of the letters can then be given a coat of spar varnish extending over the edge of the letters about one-half inch.

Fig. 63 shows an embossed letter with a plain gold outline, another black outline and a red shade. A separate letter pattern is needed for each of these, making four separate patterns. First cut the plain letter and to obtain the embossed effect, run it through an ordinary wash wringer with a sheet of sandpaper wrapped around one of the rollers. Lay this on the plain gold sheet and cut the outline; now lay these two on the sheet of black foil cutting this, and next, place these three on the red sheet and cut the shade. Fasten all together with the pasting dope.

Many designs can be made with this method, such as fish, shoes, faces, teeth, hats, pipes, etc. For example, when making a shoe, cut out the shoe and fill in all detail and shades with black shellac. If making a quantity, take the full foil sheet and with a silk screen process all details and outline and then cut out. Black process paint is used when using the silk screen. The silk screen can also be used to make matt corners, inner outlines, and in the case of illustrations, to bring out the features or detail.

CHAPTER XVIII

WORKING SURFACES

IN processing one is called upon to do work on various surfaces, such as wood, paper, tin, metal, tissues, crêpes, cloth, tire covers, glass, marble, china, bakelite, rubber, celluloid, leather, oilcloth, plasterboard, etc. The material most frequently used is the news or chip board, therefore most paint manufacturers have ground their

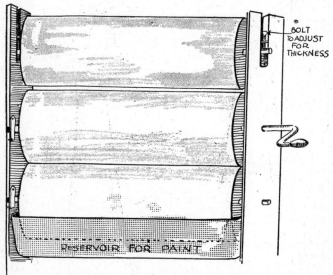

Figure 64.—An Inexpensive Coating Unit.

paint to handle this type of board. For other materials the paint will have to be prepared differently. For processing on cardboard a paint base will have to be screened or coated on. For small surfaces a wash wringer makes a handy unit for coating the board by simply placing a reservoir for the paint below the bottom roller.

A cheap coating unit for larger surfaces can be made as shown in Fig. 64. The rollers are all the same size. The bottom roller rides in the paint, placing it on the middle or coating roller. The top roller is adjustable to handle any thickness of board. Exact sizes are not mentioned as this can be made to suit any particular

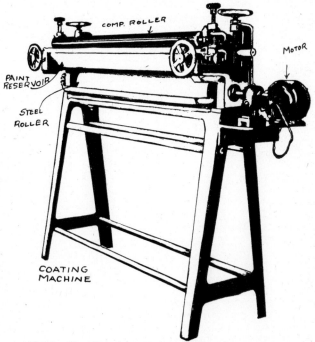

Figure 65.—Standard Type of Coating Machine.

requirements.   For the process man operating on a larger scale the regular coating machine is best.   There are several good coating machines on the market, Fig. 65 showing the make-up of the standard type.   This type requires only a quart of paint to operate, whereas others require as much as five gallons.   Such a coating machine can be used to coat paper, cardboard, tissues, crêpes, etc., and is a time-saver.

Of course to the man with limited capital this entails quite an outlay of cash as its cost runs from $500 to $800, depending upon the improvements, motors, etc.

The background color can be screened on with a screen using a coarse mesh silk, but more paint will be used this way.

CHAPTER XIX

COUNTER OR DOOR GLASS SIGNS

THIS is a very profitable field and offers unlimited possibilities. Fig. 66 shows one of this type of signs. It is 4 by 10 inches on plate glass with clipped edges. Such letters are usually of colored metallics with a black background and colored border or decorations. Most any base will do as the glass is firm and makes a flat base itself. A frame is built of 1-by-11-inch lumber, the size to be 8 by 14 inches inside measurement, allowing a 2-inch margin all around.

On this mount the silk, being sure to get it tight. On the base place a piece of the glass to be printed, this to be in the center or where it will hit the center

Figure 66.—A Glass Sign.

of the frame.   Obtain four pieces of beaverboard one inch wide, two pieces being six inches long and the other two ten inches long.   These must be of the exact thickness of the glass.   They are nailed to the base around the glass and serve to protect the screen from the sharp edges of the glass.   They are mounted as shown in Fig. 67, the bottom piece being fastened on one side to allow the glass to be placed and to replace marker piece.

Now fasten the screen to the base, being sure to have a uniform margin all around.   As the screening is to go onto the back of the glass, the entire run will have

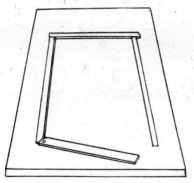

Figure 67.—Frame on Base When Running Glass.

to be reversed.   To get a good reversed copy, take the original copy, which we assume is on a sheet of paper, and against the back of this place a piece of carbon paper with the carbon side towards the paper, then trace the original.   This will give a good reverse copy to work from.   Put this in position on the blank piece of glass, lower the screen and trace onto the silk.   Fill the tracing in with the stopping-out solution and the completed screen, ready to run, will appear as in Fig. 68.   A sensitized or celluloid screen can also be used.   After the background has been run and is entirely dry, with a small brush, coat the letters that are to be metallic with a white spar varnish, and while still wet, dust on the metallics. The red outline or decoration can be screened or put on by hand. When this is dry, back with tin foil or felt. It can also be sprayed with a good durable paint, insuring longer life to the sign.

The chipped edges may be done by a glass house or

Figure 68.—Completed Screen, Ready to Run.

they may be done in the shop with a pair of pliers. Practice will enable one to do a nice clean job. These edges should be buffed to take off the sharpness, eliminating the possibility of cutting. A chain may be fastened around the sign or a sheet of metal can be placed against the back with the edges bent over where the glass has been chipped, thus holding it in place. The backing also protects the sign against the weather and makes it easy to fasten to a wall or door as holes may be placed in the backing for screws or nails. This type of sign is cheaply made and yet it may be sold at a good price.

CHAPTER XX

WINDOW BACKGROUNDS

TO THE store having a number of windows where backgrounds or plaques are used, the silk screen method will prove valuable. It may be used on any surface and it gives individuality to the display. Most stores have a sign department which can easily handle this type of work. For large backgrounds, a frame can be made of ordinary 1-by-2-inch lumber, and if exceedingly large, 2-by-2-inch lumber.

Organdy may be used instead of silk, combined with either the celluloid or paper stencils. A run of 25 can be made for about $1.25, which, if purchased in a sign shop, would cost about $7.00. One advantage in these backgrounds is that they can be made to fit the window, thus allowing a wider variety of displays. In addition to this, they can be made to harmonize with the balance of the trim. Fig. 69 shows a few of the types that can be screened. It will be noticed that a valance is shown. This is easily made as well as decorative panels and merchandise holders.

The cut-outs can be made by using an automatic cutting machine to cut out tops, designs, etc. More effective and distinctive displays are obtained by cut-outs as this does away with the straight line effect, adding much to the beauty of the display.

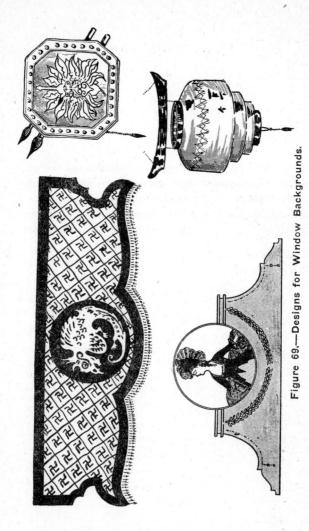

Figure 69.—Designs for Window Backgrounds.

CHAPTER XXI

PROCESSING PENNANTS, FELT ARM-BANDS, ETC.

FOR pennants, the felt can be purchased in rolls or cut to the size of the pennant. If it is planned to screen one at a time, the felt should be cut to size, but the most economical way is to screen three or four at a time and then have them cut apart. They should be cut

Figure 70.—Processed Pennants, Banners, etc.

by an electric cutter to insure a sharp cut. Fig. 70 shows some of the uses or items in this line. Many attractive effects can be obtained by adding more varnish than usual, and while the paint on the pennant is still wet, dip or spray colored metallics over it. Several shades of metallics on the same letter make an impressive and rich appearance.

Another attractive pennant or pillow can be made by dipping the wet paint on the pennant into colored wool flock. Small colored beads, sand or ground glass may also be used.

A very attractive and yet cheap display can be made by processing on crêpe paper.

PROCESSING OILCLOTH SIGNS

There is quite a demand for a permanent or semi-permanent sign which can easily be made by screening on oilcloth. As it will stand the weather and is adaptable for either inside or outside use, it is always in demand. Ice cream manufacturers and photo finishers are large users of this type of sign.

Figure 71.—Processed Oilcloth Sign.

There are two kinds of oilcloth, namely, the dull finish and gloss finish. The dull is the easier of the two to screen on, as the glossy finish has a greasy surface causing the paint to creep. This can be prevented by washing with gasoline or benzine and dusting with talcum

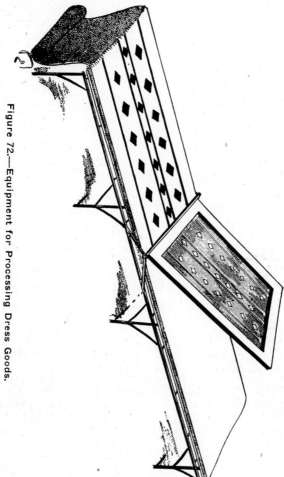

Figure 72.—Equipment for Processing Dress Goods.

powder. Large frames are necessary for this type of sign, therefore organdy should be used with a paper screen. Fig. 71 shows the type of sign referred to in this chapter.

PROCESSING DRESS GOODS, VOILES, ETC.

This is a line new to the process man but is just one of the many fields that he can take advantage of. Special equipment will be required, such as a table (Fig. 72) long enough to handle at least a 50-foot length of cloth. At the ends horses or tables can be used to place the material on until entirely dry. Fig. 73. The table, Fig. 72,

Figure 73.—Horses for Drying Processed Goods.

should be well made and covered with a good padding, felt being preferable. Over this stretch oilcloth, thus producing a good smooth base. It is also advisable to have a roll of cheap paper, this being placed on the oilcloth, acting as a blotter to absorb the paint that is forced through the cloth. This is pulled along with the cloth and will prevent mussy or dirty backs.

The screen is fastened to an axle which rides on a sliding adjusting arm which in turn rides on the tracks on each side of the table. It must be remembered that we are only printing a small space at a time and then the screen is moved on to the next spot to be printed.

Register can be had easily as a line is made on the table lengthwise and the material is matched against this for side registration. A more correct register can be had by ruling off the entire table in ½-inch squares and also the sides of the printing frame.

For example, to print a 36-inch section, start at the beginning of the roll or bolt and print the first impression; pull the screen along on the track until 36 inches is reached on the table, this to match with the top end of the printing frame; print and slide down to 72 inches, repeating until the entire bolt is screened. If one intends going into this field on a large scale, it is advisable to have large floor space.

The paint for this particular line should be purchased from a process supply house, explaining what it is intended for, as a special paint formula is required. Each material requires a special paint consistency. Heavy goods require an opaque color; silks, voiles, etc., must be screened with a paint that will not spread or ooze through the material. A transparent printers' ink can be used by adding litho varnish, but only experience with the various fabrics will show just which paint will work best on the various surfaces.

Due also to climatic conditions, humidity, etc., a set rule cannot be given, as paint has a tendency to work well under certain conditions and the same paint on the same material in a different climate will give trouble.

CHAPTER XXII

GLASS SIGNS *

GLASS sign work requires more careful workmanship and attention to detail than any other. The first operation on any wood or card sign is the last operation on a glass sign. Changing from the methods used on ordinary cardboard, metal or board sign to the glass sign is rather complex as the procedure and methods of operation are different.

A sketch or design is required as in other process work. There is the exception that if there is to be only a single sign to be made, the copy is traced directly on the face of the glass. Or it may be sketched and the sketch perforated and pounced on the glass. For sketching on glass, use a china marking pencil, red or yellow preferred.

The next operation depends upon the artist himself. In some cases outlining in black before gilding would be a cleaner cut job, while many sign painters do their gilding first, using the sketched design on the face as a guide.

A matt finish can be obtained by leaving an open space of gold towards the outer edge of the letters while the

---

* The author was aided in this section by a leading authority in this particular line who has turned out a vast number of insurance glass signs as well as the finest specimens of etched glass signs. Formulas which have been kept secret by him for years are here presented to the public for the first time.

center will be varnished, using valspar or any good grade of varnish. After the varnish is dry, gild the entire letter. The portions that were varnished will have a dull matt effect and the clear portion of the glass will be a bright gold. For making the gold leaf adhere to the glass, a water gold size is made as follows: A piece of Russian or American isinglass the size of a half dollar is put into a pint of water and. boiled ten minutes; it is then strained through a piece of cheesecloth and is ready for use. This is brushed on the glass and the gold picked up on a gilder's tip and laid on, the size holding it in place.

Gold leaf will not adhere to glass that is dirty or greasy, so to insure the glass being absolutely clean, wash

Figure 74.—Method of Laying Gold Leaf.

with a mixture of whiting water with a touch of ammonia. Apply this to the glass with a brush and wipe dry with a piece of cheesecloth. Then the glass is ready for the gold leaf, assuring a bright gold. Fig. 74 shows the method of laying the gold leaf.

There is still another method of obtaining a two-tone gold effect, but this is done by using two shades of gold leaf. First, the outer edge is gilded with a gold leaf, backed, and the center gilded with a lemon or pale gold.

After the first layer of gold is applied, it should be left to dry, then rubbed gently with cotton. This tends to brighten the gold. Giving several applications of water size will take out the check marks and make a clean, bright effect. When the holes have been patched and the sign is entirely dry, recoat with hot water mixed with a little of the water size. After burnishing again with cotton, back up the sign, using a red sable or camel-hair brush. The best backing paint is a japan color, preferably chrome orange, thinned with spar varnish and turpentine.

It must be remembered that gold leaf is semi-transparent, and if a dark color is used directly against the gold it has a tendency to kill its bright luster, therefore the chrome orange is suggested as it is the closest to the gold leaf. After this backing coat is entirely dry, brush off the surplus gold first with a piece of moist cotton dipped in pumice, and rub lightly; then rub off with a stiff brush.

Quantity signs are made on the same principle, only screens are used for the various backings, the only real hand operation being the laying of the gold leaf.

ETCHED GLASS SIGNS

The first operation in making an etched glass sign consists in coating the glass with a thin solution of turpentine asphaltum and doing the same to one side of a sheet of lead foil. When these become tacky, attach the coated side of the foil to the glass and rub out smooth with a piece of leather. It must be remembered that all work is done in reverse; therefore lay the pencil sketch on the lead foil, first coating with a little soap and wax. With a stiff brush rub the back of the sketch and the impression will be seen on the lead foil after the sketch has been removed. The stenciled side of the sketch, of course, should be placed against the foil.

Now with a stencil knife cut out the portions that are to be etched, a clean sharp cut must be made for clean etching. The centers of letters or portions to be etched are picked out or removed. The entire piece is then cleaned with naphtha or turpentine and pumice to make it grease-proof, as the acid will not etch through grease.

Next coat the opposite side of the glass as well as the edges with a heavy coat of asphaltum or parafine which has been heated to a liquid. Apply with a brush. The glass is now ready for etching.

The etching tank is a box made of heavy wood, about ten inches high by six feet long and three feet wide. This is treated with several coats of asphaltum, or better, lined with lead. The lead tank is much better, but will cost considerably more.

Etching acid, to insure keeping it to a good consistency, should be removed from the tank when the etching is finished and kept in a lead carboy. Hydrofluoric acid, about 48% or 52%, is used and should be about an inch above the glass which would necessitate about an inch and a half of acid in the tank.

The sign to be etched is placed in this tank, foil side up, with a little ground mica sprinkled over it. Various grades or sizes of the mica give a coarse or even etch. Etch for five or six minutes, remove from tank and wash off with water, then replace in tank and reëtch for eight minutes. Wash with hot water, thus removing the lead foil and parafine coating. The glass is rewashed with the whiting water and ammonia before gilding.

The leaf is applied and then backed with the backing paint and it is ready for the varnish backing.

PROCESS ETCHED GLASS SIGNS

To make etched glass signs in quantity, the following routine will be found to be the most reliable. An etching plate is required and it is made as follows: a piece of plate glass is treated with asphaltum for a master, and lead foil applied as for making an etched glass sign. The design is etched or transferred onto this glass. For the master plate the design is in reverse of the finished signs to be made. In other words, the parts to be etched on the master sign are those not to be etched on the finished sign. When completed this master sign will be the plate from which an impression will be made with an acid-resisting ink onto the glass to make the other signs. Acid-resisting ink is made as follows:

½ lb. paraffine	1 lb. beeswax
7 oz. rosin	2 oz. Egyptian asphaltum dry
½ oz. Venice turps	16 oz. turpentine

Heat the wax and paraffine in a container; heat rosin and asphaltum in another container; pour both together

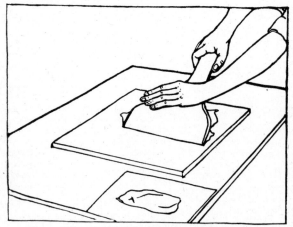

Figure 75.—Spreading Ink over Master Plate.

and add Venice turps; strain while hot and add turpentine. Keep stirring to avoid separation until chilled. If properly made, this solution when cool will have the consistency of butter.

This ink is spread over the master plate with a wide scraping knife, the ink going into the etched portion. It is then scraped off of the unetched portions. Fig. 75. A sheet of tissue paper is placed over this master plate and rubbed with a stiff brush picking up the ink. See Fig. 76.

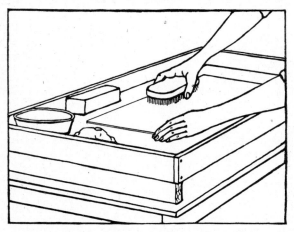

Figure 76.—Picking Up Ink from Master Plate.

This inked tissue should be air-dried about three minutes before being placed on the sign to be etched. It is brushed, ink side down, onto the blank glass (Fig. 77) with a shoe brush and left to dry for about 18 hours. This same operation is used for each sign to be etched and it requires very little time when the knack of brushing is obtained. The tissue is then removed, first soaking it with a solution of 75 per cent alcohol and 25 per cent water. The tissue can be easily lifted off. Each sign is then placed into the acid tank and etched. When cleaned, lay the gold

Figure 77.—Transferring Tissue with Ink to Blank Glass.

leaf and make a master plate for the backing. This is made the same as the first master plate, only the ink for backing is made as follows:

1 lb. beeswax	1 lb. yellow ochre japan
5 oz. cherry rosin	½ oz. Venice turps
4 oz. turpentine	4 oz. interior spar varnish

Heat the wax and rosin in separate containers and when heated add the yellow ochre with Venice turps and the turpentine and varnish; stir well and strain. It is then ready for use.

This ink is used the same as the acid ink, scraping it onto the master plate, transferring it to the tissue by brushing and then onto the gilded sign. Register is obtained by little crosses which are etched into each sign. The background color covers these so they are not seen when the sign is completed. Various colors can be made with this method, but it is best to use a silk screen to fill in a background. Fig. 78 shows a method for screening which produces perfect register. A heavy piece of plate

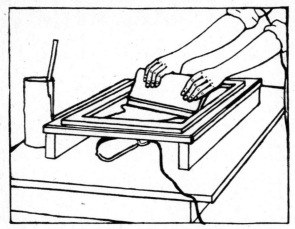

Figure 78.—Perfect Register, Using Electric Light.

glass is placed on blocks beneath which an electric light is placed. The worker can then see through the various colors, showing just where to place the screen, also showing pinholes, etc., if the color has not covered properly.

COLORS, PAINTS, ETC., FOR GLASS SIGNS

Paints for glass signs must be of an entirely different consistency and base than for the average card job. Cheap colors will not run properly, will not last, and the color will not be brilliant or attractive.

The mixture and vehicle used depends entirely on the nature of the color. Leads, chromes, siennas and umbers are natural driers and do not need force-drying with japan. In many cases they will need retarding. Reds, blues and black will need special attention. The following is suggested:

Black—50% ivory black in japan and 50% drop black in oil with inside spar varnish and turpentine. In moderate weather this is an overnight drier.

Toluidine Red—20% red in japan, 80% red in oil.   Add
   turpentine.
Blue-Cobalt—Ultramarine, Prussian and milori blue are
   slow driers and need speeding by a formula of 30%
   japan color and 70% oil color.   Vehicle used for
   this is 75% oil and 25% turpentine.

It is not advisable to use ultramarine on glass, as in
most cases this color will mottle and chalk, and when
exposed to changing atmospheric conditions and sunlight,
it is sure to check.   The sulphuric acid used in making
this color is seldom washed thoroughly enough to make
it permanent.   If this shade of blue is demanded, suggest using cobalt blue, and by careful mixing with Prussian blue, this tint can be obtained.

Chrome greens are natural drying colors.   Emerald
and Paris green will need a 50% japan and 50% oil
formula with 75% spar and 25% turpentine.

The opacity in some colors is so great that most paint
manufacturers grind a 25% color with 75% barium sulphate.   This is where the trouble on glass signs arises.
Calcium carbonate magnesium and calcium phosphate or
any other varieties used in loading colors is dangerous
to the glass sign man.   Colors should be close to 100%
chemically pure.   A 25% chrome will check in 30 days
if applied to glass.   This has a starry appearance and
will fade out to a mottled gray in time.   Chrome oxides
are very durable, and where a transparent green is
wanted, we suggest Mite's green medium made by Devoe.
This is a very permanent color.   Violets or purples are
sold by a few manufacturers in oil or japan, but are not
sunfast.   Tests have proven that they will last as long
as six months, but for a longer period it is unsafe.   The
most durable colors on glass are blacks, grays, toluidine
red (100% C. P.), chrome green, siennas, ochres and
umbers, including Venetian red.   Cobalt blue or ultrama-

rine should never be mixed with lead. Use zinc white instead. Coal tar red should never be mixed with any other color, but should be used straight. Madder lake, alizarine lake and toluidine red can be brought down with zinc white to make pink.

When a white background is wanted, use 75% lead and 25% zinc white brought down with boiled oil and turpentine. This will make a very durable white. Double coating adds 100% to its life and durability. When transparency in colors is desired, use regular shades of colors only, adding 20% aluminum hydrate (a printer's medium). This extender will not affect the colors. When an opaque black is wanted, use a 25% carbon black, which has three times the strength of any other black. This black will be found very essential when it is to be used for a background for an electrical sign where opacity is required. Cadmium yellows are most permanent and should be used in preference to chrome yellow. They are very rich in tone and are very durable. English vermilion is scarcely used today, due to its being an imported color not always available and being too expensive, the results not being worth the price. Toluidine red is a very successful substitute and has been proved to be more permanent. A non-bleeding red only should be used on glass. Any shade of red can be mixed by adding alizarine toner or chrome orange. Fire reds can be used for lighter tones, these also being non-bleeding colors. There is also on the market now a non-bleeding maroon, or rose lake, which is permanent. Mention is made of these various bleeding colors, as most of all trouble on glass can be traced to color. Leads have a chemical reaction on bleeding reds. By using zinc alone one runs into danger of the paint cracking and chipping.

CHAPTER XXIII

PROCESSING DECALCOMANIA SIGNS

DECALCOMANIA signs are designs that are printed, lithographed or painted on a sheet of paper that has been treated with a paste solution. When the sign is moistened and pressed against the surface intended for it, the paste will soften, allowing the paper to be slid off, leaving the printed portion on the surface.

If lithographed or printed in colors, a large quantity is required to make it a paying proposition, but with the silk screen method, several hundred can be run at a profit.

The best way to start is to buy from a paper house the standard decalcomania paper, or duplex, as it is known. It is an imported article and all houses do not carry it. If it is impossible to buy it, this paper can be made, but will not prove as desirable as the purchased variety. It is made as follows:

A sheet 20 by 30 inches is the best size. A good smooth paper is necessary. This is coated with a solution of starch and gum arabic, using it thin. When this is dry, re-coat. Lay the sheets on a flat surface to dry, as hanging will curl them. When dry, pack one on top of another and leave for several days to season.

Fig. 79 shows a design of which we are to make a decalcomania. This is a 4-color job. The first run will be a coat of tough pale varnish or gloss oil. This is to protect the color as another coat of varnish is screened on the completed job, thereby leaving the paint between two layers of

Figure 79.—Design for a Decalcomania.

varnish. The screen for the varnish is made $1/16$ inch larger than the design. This same screen may also be used for the last coat of varnish. On this coat of varnish the cream paint is the first color run. A good grade of color is advisable to eliminate pinholes. Also to this paint add a little gold ink varnish. The next color is flesh, then red, and last, the outline screen which is black.

It must be remembered that the varnish will always have a tendency to be "tacky," so when packing, place a piece of waxed paper over each copy. If this is done it will eliminate a lot of trouble due to copies sticking.

In the case of a "slide off" decalcomania, all colors

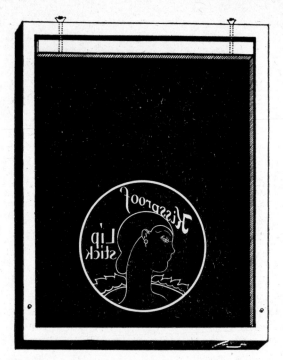

Figure 80.—Screen for a "Slide Off" Decalcomania.

are run in reverse. By this is meant after the first varnish coat has been screened, the black outline is run in
reverse. The screen will appear as Fig. 80. All other
colors are screened onto this first outline copy. This does
not require a close register as the outline acts as a register.
When the job is run all that will be seen is the backing.
This type is for outside use and is usually put on the outside of windows or trucks, etc. It is slid off the paper instead of the paper being removed from the paint.

Only by experimenting can you obtain the best results,
as the prints, if not properly made, will not release from

the paper, or may crack. It is wise to consult a paint supply house to secure the proper paints and varnishes.

SPECIAL TRUCK AND WAGON DECALCOMANIAS

Decalcomania transfers for outside work, such as trucks, board signs, etc., are made on a heavy duplex transfer paper. This is a double paper and will be more fully described in the instructions for applying.

The screens may be either photo, lacquer or knife-cut on thin vellum paper or combination of these. A description of the method most frequently and successfully used follows. It is a combination of knife-cut and hand-cut lacquer screens.

Suppose that the transfer to be made is an inscription reading "Model Dairy Company" with a gold letter and a black outline. The first step is to make a full-sized accurate layout of the whole design. This may be drawn in pencil on a piece of white poster paper or wrapping paper.

Take a sheet of thin vellum paper or a good grade of tracing paper and carefully trace the outline of the letters, using a fairly hard pencil in order to get a thin, clean-cut line. Before making this tracing, make four crosses about half an inch long, one on each corner of the layout, about one inch from the outside of the lettering, these being the markers or points from which registration is obtained. These will be found to aid materially in both the making of the screen and in printing. When making the outline tracing on the vellum paper include these crosses or registers. Now turn the tracing over so that the lettering is reversed, and give the paper two coats of shellac. The stencil may be cut on either sheet zinc, glass or cardboard. Glass is best and it is given a coat of wax composed of equal parts of beeswax, kerosene, and linseed oil. This is heated in a double boiler and the glass is coated with the mixture which acts as a cushion to cut on and it also holds the letters flat to the glass. Centers will not be "off center" if this method is used. The shellaced tracing is laid on this and smoothed out by pulling a squeegee over it or rubbing down with a piece of leather, working from the center to the outside edges. The tracing or outline is now cut out with a stencil knife.

After the stencil is cut the screen is laid over it, keeping the design centered on the screen, which should be of a coarse mesh silk, from number two to number eight.

The screen is now ironed with a hot iron, using a sheet of paper or cloth beneath the iron. This vulcanizes the tracing to the screen. The iron must not be too hot or it will scorch the paper, making it brittle and cracking it.

After the tracing is ironed to the screen it should be gently rubbed with a rag saturated with gasoline, kerosene or naphtha, to clean off the surplus wax.

This screen is now ready for printing. The object of making this particular screen a knife-cut stencil is to insure a sharp edge. A hand lacquer screen would give a mesh edge. The screen for the gold center and the varnish edging are hand-cut in lacquer stencil on a 12XX or 13XX silk. This type screen is thinner and places a thinner layer of paint on the surface than the paper screen.

The lacquer screen and knife-cut screen are both traced from the original sketch. The best method for perfect register is to pull a proof from the outlined stencil which has been run first. Lay this beneath the screen and trace an outline $\frac{1}{16}$ inch all around. This will give a perfect screen for the varnished outline. Next the screen for the gold center is placed over the outlined proof and traced with a fine line right on the center of the outlines of the proof. This will give the gold center with the dark outline.

The screens are now ready for printing and the varnish is first. Place a sheet of the duplex paper against the guides, lower the screen and run with a sharp squeegee as in ordinary process work. The varnish to be used for this must be a heavy-bodied, tough drying varnish, pale in color, so that it will not dull the colors. By running the varnish first as well as last, the paint and the gold which form the letters are sandwiched between the two films of varnish and the weather has no chance to affect the gold bronze and discolor it. Gold bronze will always dull and tarnish if exposed to the air. This method also eliminates the necessity of giving the transfer a coat of varnish after it is applied to the truck or surface. An additional coat of varnish, of course, will make it more durable.

After the varnish has been run, the varnish screen is set aside until it is used for the final back-up coat.

The next screen to be run is the black outline, and for this use a paste paint ground in oil, with heavy-bodied varnish added. The register marks on the outline screen are registered over the marks on the sheets of decalcomania paper which contain the varnish impression and the outline is printed. Now the gold screen is set in position and the gold is run, using a good grade of gold screening bronze mixed with bronzing liquid with a touch of gold ink varnish. Finally the varnish screen, which is run first, is again run, thus backing and sealing up the letters.

In mixing paints for transfers, use little or no drier as they will make the letters brittle and take the life out of the paint. When the last varnish coating is dry, the transfers are dusted with talcum powder and a sheet of wax paper is placed between them to prevent sticking.

Duplex decalcomania paper is a double paper made by using a fairly heavy smooth white paper as a base to which a thin tissue paper is pasted with a weak paste

solution.   Then the face of the tissue paper is coated
with a paste and gum arabic solution.

To apply these transfers first locate the center mark
and horizontal lines on the surface to which they are
to be applied.   Then take a transfer and by rubbing the
corner of it between the thumb and forefinger, the backing paper is loosened from the tissue.   Do not take this
backing paper off, but just start to peel it from the tissue,
so that when the transfer is against the desired surface it
will be easy to take hold of the corner and peel it off.
Now lay the transfer down and give the letters a coat of
quick drying varnish.   It does not matter if the varnish
extends over the letters a little as any surplus may be
wiped off after the transfer is in position.   The main
objective is to give the letters a good coat of varnish
covering completely.   When the varnish becomes tacky,
put the transfer in position, marks having been put on
the surface first to insure its being placed right.   The
transfer will not stand a lot of shifting as the varnish
is tacky and is apt to pull the letters off.   The window
or background is slightly dampened before the transfer
is applied and must be clean and free from grease.

When the transfer is in position, smooth it out with a
rubber roller or with a soft rag.   Now carefully peel the
backing off, wetting with a damp rag as you go along.
This will leave the tissue paper on the window with
the lettering.

Roll this well, being sure there are no bubbles or
wrinkles.   Now take a sponge and with clean water
saturate the tissue backing.   Carefully peel this off and
again roll with a rubber roller, wetting first.   Wash the
design with a sponge.   This will take off the gum with
which the decalcomania tissue has been coated.   This
should be done as quickly as possible; otherwise the
edges of the letters will curl up.

Another way to apply these transfers is to use a solution of one part alcohol and one part water in place of the varnish. First saturate a rag in this solution and wipe over the glass or board surface. Now wipe the entire surface of the transfer with this solution and immediately put the transfer in position, proceeding exactly as described in the varnish method. If after smoothing the transfer any bubbles appear, prick them with a pin, letting the air out and re-roll with a wet roller.

CHAPTER XXIV

HOW TO MAKE SUNLIGHT SIGNS

THE outstanding feature of the sunlight sign is that it requires no upkeep or attention after it is once installed and it has all the advantages of an electric sign without the use of electricity.

Although they are used almost exclusively on trucks and wagons, this field can be extended to many other uses. They can be used in front of a store, on buildings and on posts.

The sign is painted in reverse on a sheet of frosted glass. This leaves the letters open and allows the light to filter onto a mirror which is set at an angle. This tends to magnify the light, giving it a sparkle that is very attractive. Even though the mirror is on an angle the sign will appear to be straight up and down. This is an optical illusion which has been used for years by magicians in various tricks, such as the spider woman, half woman, etc.

Fig. 81 shows the make-up of the sign. The sizes mentioned are not standard but are given as an illustration. Fig. 82 shows the method of installation on the cab of a truck.

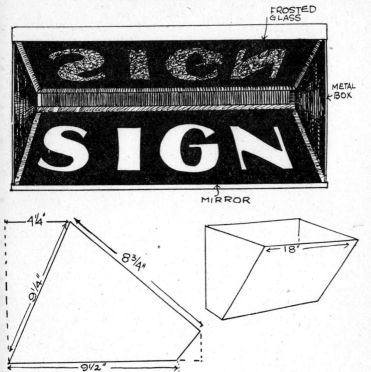

Figure 81.—Construction of a Sunlight Sign.

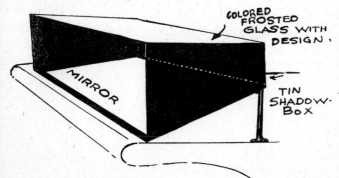

Figure 82.—Installation of a Sunlight Sign.

CHAPTER XXV

PROCESSING TIRE COVERS

A COVER on a tire today is a necessity and not a
novelty, as was the case a few years ago. Many
new cars are equipped with a tire cover with either the
name of the car or the dealer's name and address on it.
During political campaigns thousands are used. The silk
screen process of printing these is practically the only
method that can be used to turn out a good durable job.
Printing or painting by other methods is easily washed
off or painted over. It is impossible to remove the imprint from the tire cover that has been baked, as to use
removers would naturally ruin the cover. There are several varieties in shape, namely, drum, half-drum, and
slip-on covers. The drum type covers the entire tire,
and the center makes a large solid surface for an adver-
tisement. The half-drum covers the entire tire and half
of the center opening. The slip-on covers the tire only.
For processing on tire covers it is necessary to obtain the
top panel before it is sewed together. It is best when
making the design to first obtain one of the sewed
finished covers and on this paint the copy. The blank
panels are larger than when sewed and in making the
design on these one is apt to make it too large. The
screen is made from the painted sample, using either a
paper or a celluloid sheet screen, thus giving a much
neater job, because the surface is usually so glossy that

any ragged edge can be easily seen. Registering is difficult in quantity runs where a letter has an outline, or in
a monogram where close registry is necessary. The
panels are cut by electric cutters in large batches at a
time, the cutter being guided by hand, and it is impossible
to cut them uniformly. When several colors are to be
run, proceed as follows: Take one of the blank panels
and over this lay a sheet of tracing paper and cut this
tracing paper exactly uniform to the blank panel. Now
take this tracing paper and lay it over the painted sample
and trace the design onto the tracing paper in exact detail. Color in as per the copy and mount this on a sheet
of cardboard and cut out the same as the tracing or

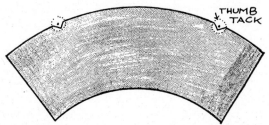

Figure 83.—Markers Used in Processing Tire Covers.

transparent paper. This is to be laid on top of the blank
panel to make sure that it is exactly the same. Lay this
on the working base and affix the registers, these to remain for the entire job. Lower the screen and trace the
first color. Run this color and then relay this tracing
into position and trace the second color—do the same with
each color.

Another method is to have the cutter cut on the panels
a small V which will not damage the cover, as the sewing
will hide it. This is laid on the working base and small
thumb tacks or wedge markers are fastened into the cut.
Fig. 83. It will be found that fairly good register can be
obtained this way, only care must be taken in printing that

the squeegee does not run over these tacks as it may move them and possibly tear the screen. Run the squeegee, preferably a small window squeegee that has been cut to size, in a semi-circle, as in Fig. 84.

The paint for this work is somewhat different from ordinary process paint and in purchasing it specify "tire-cover" paint.

One of the most important items is baking. The purpose of this is to soften the cover sufficiently to allow the process paint to amalgamate with the cover, preventing peeling, chipping or being removed. Special ovens are built, also special racks. These are made of metal

Figure 84.—Operation of the Squeegee.

and the oven is made so that the rack which should be on wheels can be rolled into it. Gas is used and should not be turned on too high, as excessive heat will scorch and turn the color of the paint. The temperature should not be more than 200 degrees, an average of 180 is best. For the man desiring to make a specialty of this line, it is advisable to make a stock set of screens for the various car trade-marks, the dealer's name being stenciled on with a separate screen. This will allow a two-color job without much preparation.

It is good practice to wipe each blank pattern with benzine, as it is apt to contain grease on the surface, either from the coating process or from handling.

There are certain leather substitutes that are used for

tire covers that will discolor white or any light-colored paint. These are to be avoided unless an aluminum is dusted on, and if the surface is of a varnish nature, the aluminum or bronze is apt to stick to the surface, making an awful mess that is impossible to clean up.

Another way and the most practical to get a good register is to have a piece of cardboard (square) and on this affix the piece of material that is to be processed on, using just a daub of rubber cement on the corners. In this way a perfect register may be obtained, the material being removed from the cardboard allowing the re-use of the board for future runs. The rubber cement will not damage nor mar the cover material.

CHAPTER XXVI

STENCILS FOR THE HOME

THE occasion arises often for decorating or trimming furniture and various things about the home and little skill is required to do this sort of work. The design may be taken from a newspaper or magazine and can easily be traced by anyone and with a knife cut out into the form of a stencil. As lacquer paints dry so rapidly, spraying is advisable. An air brush is best suited, but the price is prohibitive for an ordinary job. An efficient substitute is an insect sprayer which sells for about 50 cents. This device, Fig. 85, will lay

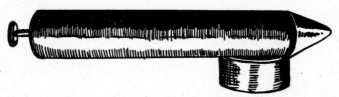

Figure 85.—Insect Sprayer for Lacquer.

the lacquer on evenly and will not smear or mess up everything.

The best material for the stencil is celluloid, which may be purchased from a stationer or art shop. Old photographic films may be used by soaking off the solution in warm water. The celluloid sheet is laid over the design selected and cut out with a sharp-pointed knife.

Small "ties" should be left to strengthen the stencil and eliminate tearing. Various forms of stencils and possibilities are shown in Fig. 86.

It is best when cutting to have a piece of glass or sheet

Figure 86.—Stencil Designs for Home Use.

zinc as a base, which gives a good cutting surface and also acts as a cushion.

When cutting be sure and cut on a slight slant inward, as this will prevent the paint from seeping under the stencil when stenciling.

First obtain a piece of newspaper and cut out a piece in the center that will allow the stencil to lie on top of it, as shown in Fig. 87. This is to prevent the paint from spraying over the edge of the stencil. Tack it or hold it in place with adhesive tape, and spray as in Fig. 87.

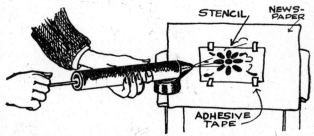

Figure 87.—Operation of Hand Spray.

It is advisable to have someone hold the stencil down with a stick, as blurry edges will result if the stencil is not tight against the base. The design should be centered before stenciling, as a design not properly centered is "side-heavy" and looks amateurish. A two-color effect can be obtained by stenciling one color and then shifting the stencil about one eighth of an inch and stenciling with another color. This will make a shade or high light and has a most pleasing effect. To produce two or three colors, certain small sections are cut out on all stencils, registration being obtained by these. Care must be taken when removing the stencil from the stenciled article as a little rub will smear the entire job.

The lacquer to use for this type of work is the standard

spraying lacquer, being thinned if necessary with lacquer thinner.   Lacquer that has been dropped on clothing or hands can easily be removed with the lacquer thinner.

The lacquer and thinner have an odor that is apt to affect some people, therefore it is advisable to do this work in an attic or well ventilated room.

CHAPTER XXVII

COMBINATION PROCESS AND ETCHED BRASS SIGNS

THIS type of sign has always found favor with doctors, dentists, and lawyers. It is also being used extesively by banks above their various cages. It is made as follows: The sheet brass is first buffed, handling it after this only on the edges, not touching the face of the brass. The portions to be etched are screened on the brass, using, instead of the ordinary stencil paint, Pitman's etching ink and powdered with Zinssers white. The plate is then placed in an oven and heated to set the ink. If the letters are to be etched, the background is screened onto the brass with the etching ink. These portions so covered will resist the acid etching out the open portions. If the letters only are to be etched, a bank of beeswax and asphaltum is placed on top around the edge to keep the acid from running over the sides. If the background is to be etched a frame is made and the beeswax putty banked to the edge. The etching solution consists of one part nitric acid to three parts water. This is poured onto the plate to cover well and allowed to stand overnight. The acid is then poured into the wax bottle and kept for future use, the sign being washed with clear water. The etching ink is then removed by heating and then washed clean with a solution of kerosene and benzine. Outlines or shades can then be screened on. The etched portions can then be colored by painting or stippling, wiping or scraping off around edges. Before shipping, clean the sign with a solution of oxalic acid and water.

CHAPTER XXVIII

HANDY SHOP NOTES

To Make Stencil Paper

Use ordinary manilla paper and coat both sides with one part kerosene, one part boiled oil. When dry, shellac both sides, this being done after copy has been traced on. When stencil has been cut, shellac top side.

How to Mark on Celluloid

Use anhydrous acetic acid, adding the shade of aniline dye color desired.

How to Stop Crawling or Creeping

Wipe the surface of the material to be processed with either curled hair or wet rag and pumice, following with damp chamois, then when screening add a little vinegar to the paint.

To Frost Mirrors

To a pint of vinegar or beer add ½ lb. of epsom salts; let dissolve and apply to mirror with a brush. For permanent frost, varnish with white damar varnish.

To Revive Gold Size if too Dry to Gild

With a piece of cotton saturated with grain alcohol go over sized portions, doing only a little at a time.

Cement for Glass Signs

One part gum acacia to four parts water, mix, adding plaster of paris until a thick paste is obtained. Apply to both edges to be cemented.

How to Make Paint and Varnish Remover

In one gal. of benzol (full strength) dissolve one

pound powdered parafine wax. Let stand overnight add
½ gal. alcohol and ½ gal. acetone.

How to Polish Glass

Mix benzine and calcined magnesia to a paste and
polish with a soft rag.

How to Make Luminous Paints

Mix phosphorus with white damar varnish. For ink,
mix phosphorus with water. For a better grade use
calcium sulphide with varnish, grinding in a mill.

Luminous White Paint

Grind in a mill 3 oz. boiled oil, 2¾ oz. barium sulphate, 6 oz. white zinc sulphide, 3 oz. prepared calcium
carbonate, and 18 oz. luminous calcium sulphide.

To Make a Silvering Fluid

1½ gal. water, 5½ oz. silver nitrate, 10 oz. sodium
hyposulphite, 6 oz. ammonium chloride, 3 oz. prepared
chalk. Apply with a soft brush and if a heavy backing
is desired re-coat when dry. Clean glass well before
coating with silvering solution, using water with a little
nitric acid.

How to Make Mucilage

1 lb. brown dextrine, 4 oz. gum arabic, 4 oz. acetic
acid, 4 oz. alcohol, 1 qt. water. Dissolve the dextrine
in water and boil, strain through thin cloth, add the acetic
acid, let cool, then add the alcohol.

How to Make Banana Oil

Amyl acetate and benzine in equal amounts, adding
powdered pyroxilin.

How to Make Sealing Wax

To 8 oz. rosin add 1 oz. rosin turpentine, 5 oz.
bleached shellac, 1½ oz. German vermilion, 10 oz. heavy
spar, 5 oz. light spar, 1 oz. oil of turpentine. Heat on a
slow fire pouring into molds when dissolved, oiling molds
before pouring hot solution into them.

How to Make Lacquer for Brass

1 gal. 98% alcohol, 4 oz. seed lac, 4 oz. annato, 4 oz. dragons blood, 4 oz. gambole, 1 oz. saffron. Use this as a varnish, applying with a soft brush.

TO PRINT ON CURVED OR BOWL-SHAPED SURFACES

Globe shades, bowls, bulbs or any variety of curved surface can be lettered by the silk screen process. It is impossible to get a screen to fit a curved surface, so we first paint the copy onto the surface to be worked upon, and when dry, take a sheet of thin transparent paper and make a tracing. This is to get the proper shape of the letters on the curved surface. If it were laid out on a flat surface the letters would appear crooked and out of shape. It will be found that in some cases the paper will have to be cut in some places to get it flat against the surface. The design is then traced in reverse onto the silk screen. The screen is then made in the regular manner. Run the job on a very thin sheet of tissue paper. The paint should be of average consistency and loaded with fat oil gold size. The tissue sheet is laid aside until fairly tacky and then placed onto the surface desired and rubbed slightly. Now soak the tissue paper with water and peel it off.

PART II

CHAPTER XXIX

THE MIRROR OUTLINE GLASS SIGN

THE use of mirror in glass advertising signs has come into popularity recently and the processor has found a profitable item in their manufacture. Fig. X-1 shows the type of sign most generally used. It is possible to use it both as an electric sign or an opaque display. The display consists of a mirror outlined, opaque black background, with red, white and green letters.

Figure X1.—Mirror Outline Glass Electric Sign.

The first operation is to make the drawing and either have a reverse photostatic copy made, or make a pencil drawing in reverse. I have found that by making my original drawing on a light weight paper, placing a piece of carbon paper (carbon side to the back of drawing) under the original and by going over the original with a hard pencil you will get a good reverse copy to work from. This is then mounted on a sheet of cardboard the same size as the glass upon which the design is to be run or it may be mounted onto one of the sheets of glass.

The glass to be used for the job is covered with a silver nitrate or mirror solution without the protective backup and should be purchased from a glass house doing this special type of silvering. The term by which it is most generally known is a "mirror shock." Great care must be exercised in handling the glass as any finger marks or scratches on the mirror side will show up later.

The stencil is cut with any of the various methods, preferably the profilm or photographic method. On this particular job the first screen is the mirror outline. All parts that are shown in the mirror are cut out. When the screen is finished, the job is run onto the mirror side of the glass with an acid resisting paint. A good medium is zinc white ground in varnish. This is tinted with a little black or blue to make pin holes more easily detected. A good grade of acid resisting paint may be purchased already prepared from the various process supply houses.

When the paint is dry it is ready for etching, the average drying time being about 10 hours. An acid tank can easily be made by taking a wooden box that will hold water and coating it inside and out with a few coats of pitch or asphaltum.

Etching is done by making a solution of 50% nitric acid and 50% distilled or rain water. Waters having various chemical or metallic deposits are detrimental to the successful operation of etching. The glass is placed in this solution until the mirror solution starts to leave the glass. Some glass requires a longer time in the bath than others due to the mirror solution not being uniform. Only experimenting can tell the exact length of time for submersion. It must be immediately washed in running water, using a wide brush of soft hair to clean the surface and dried at once as any acid or scum remaining along the edges of the letters will gradually eat away the backup. It should then be placed in racks (see Fig. X-2) and left until ready for the next operation.

The next operation is the black or backup background

color. If it is for an opaque display, one backup is sufficient, but if the job is to be used with a shadow box this color must be handled very carefully as it must be absolutely opaque. If it is not solid enough it must be re-run to cover up pin holes that would otherwise be sure to show when a light is placed behind it.

The remaining colors or letter designs are then screened on a simple patch screen. If it is to be used with a

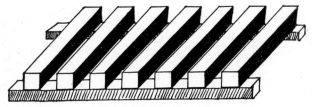

Figure X2.—Glass Rack.

shadow box, the colors best suited are colors ground in varnish and thinned with a good crystal white varnish which will give a good clear transparency. On this job (Fig. X-1) we would screen the acid resist, then etch, then the black opaque background, then screen the red, next the green and then the white is sprayed on over the entire surface. The purest white for this purpose is Devoe and Raynolds pure zinc white ground in vernosite varnish thinned with turpentine. A sprayed white is always more desirable than a screened white as screening has a tendency to show the mesh marks. Many beautiful effects may be obtained by using a clear air dry crystal lacquer sprayed to fill the letters. This lacquer may be tinted with special lacquer dyes to any desired shade.

In running glass it must be remembered that the sharp edges and corners of the glass will cut or tear the silk. To prevent this, tape is mounted on the bottom of the screen where the edges or corners ride against it. Another method is to glue strips of wood of the same thickness as the glass on the bottom side of the screen around the edges of the glass.

Another thing to remember is that glass will not be cut uniform thereby making registration difficult. The best means of obtaining a perfect register is with metal markers (see Fig. X-3). A good base board for glass work is also shown, the light under the glass base showing immediately all pin holes or misregisters.

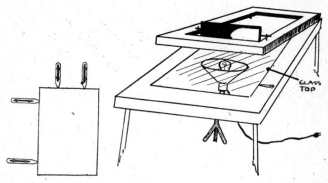

Figure X3.—Left—Markers for Glass. Right—Glass Top Table With Light Underneath.

ACID ETCHING

There are various types of etched glass signs but the acid etch or hot glue etch are most generally used. In quantity reproductions the acid etch is far the best. If an ordinary etch (which is an even surface etch) is desired, the procedure is as follows: Fig. X-4 is the sign to be reproduced. It consists of a gold letter with the center etched and an opaque black background.

The first step is to make a drawing in reverse of the entire sign including that portion that is to be etched. Then make a stencil for the portion to be etched. The stencil should be made so that the portion that is to be etched will be the portion left on the screen, as the stop out. As in (Fig. X-4), the lettering would be affixed to the screen and the open background would be the printing surface. This is printed on the glass up to about ½ inch from the edge of the glass with the following: to one gallon of any good acid resisting paint, add ¼ pint Venice turps, ½ pint Devoe vernosite varnish and ½ lb. dry powdered as-

Figure X4.—Glass Etched Sign.

phaltum. Mix well and screen this the same as any other paint. This mixture has withstood an acid dip in 100% hydrofluoric acid for two hours. When the screening of the resist is completed, place a layer of beeswax around the portion to be etched as in Fig. X-5. This will prevent the necessity of protecting the entire surface against the

BEESWAX
Figure X5.—Beeswax in Position on Resist.

acid. Pour the solution of 50% acid (hydrofluoric) and 50% water on the glass, just covering the surface. Let it stand from 15 to 45 minutes depending upon the depth of the etch desired. If the solution of acid is too strong it will burn the glass. By adding 2 ammonia cubes to a quart of acid, a clearer etch is obtained. If a frost or cloud etch is desired, mica crystals are sprinkled on the glass while it is etching.

The acid from these signs may be again used by placing it back into the lead carboy. Wash the glass well with running water, remove the beeswax and soak the entire glass in lacquer thinner, paint remover or lye water to remove the acid resist backup.

The black background is then screened on, leaving space

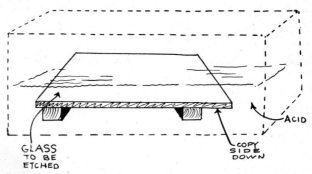

GLASS TO BE ETCHED

COPY SIDE DOWN

ACID

Figure X6.—Acid Tank With Glass in Position for Drop or Heavy Break Etch.

for the clear gold outline. Either gold bronze or gold leaf may then be applied and it is backed up with any good gray backup paint or with a gray oxide metal primer.

The other and more attractive etch is the break etch, where the glass breaks out instead of biting or frosting. The operation for this is similar to the above except that the entire surface of the glass is covered with the acid resist paint, not only on the side to be etched, but the face side is given two coats of solid acid resist paint. Then the edges are given two coats with a liquid asphaltum applied with a brush. It is then placed in the acid tank, the side to be etched down, the glass being elevated from the bottom of the tank by two 1-inch sticks. See Fig. X-6. This is left for from ½ to 2 hours depending on the type of etch desired. The acid solution is the same as mentioned in the previous article and all other operations are similar. Great care must be taken in handling this acid as it is one of the most dangerous of acids and will destroy anything it comes in contact with. It should be kept only in lead or wax carboys. All glass used in this type of etching should at least be of double strength and preferably plate.

CHAPTER XXX

THE TUSCHE METHOD

TO obtain dry brush effects and pen and ink reproductions, no finer method can be utilized than the Tusche method. The lithographers Tusche may be obtained from Naz Dar Co., Chicago, Illinois, or any lithographers supply house. The use of Tusche in silk screen making is as follows: Place the original drawing in place on the base in exact register and lower the screen (new silk being preferable as it allows a better vision of the drawing). With either a brush or pen, copy with the Tusche those portions that are to be printed. Allow to dry thoroughly. Make a solution of 50% LePages liquid glue and 50% water. This solution may have to be altered according to climatic conditions. The consistency should be such that when poured onto the screen the glue will not seep or drip through the meshes of the silk. The consistency will also have to be varied according to the mesh of the silk you are using. After the glue has been thinned with water, to each pint of mixture add one teaspoon of glycerine and mix well.

Pour this mixture on one end of the stencil and with a piece of cardboard, rubber or similar article, squeegee the glue over the entire surface of the silk design. Do not place too heavy a deposit of the mixture on the screen but simply enough to place a film on the top of the silk to fill the meshes. When dry repeat with a second coat and put it aside until it is dry.

When absolutely dry soak both sides of the screen with turpentine. With a rag saturated with turpentine lightly rub out those portions where the Tusche has been placed. After drying, the screen is ready for use. To clean the screen remove all paint and clean with kerosene, dry thoroughly and wash out the stop out backing with running water. Never use hot water as it kills the life of the silk. Another good solvent is carbon tetrachloride.

CHAPTER XXXI

THE CARBON TISSUE METHOD

THE carbon tissue method of making photographic stencils has aroused a good deal of interest in the process trade. There is nothing new about carbon tissue as it has been used in photography for many years.

Beautiful stencils, perfect in every detail, even down to the smallest of lettering, may be made with this method. However, due to the great distortion which takes place in one or all of the various steps in making this type of stencil, it is not recommended for general use. Many of the large process display manufacturers have discontinued its use after a thorough trial due to lack of control of distortion. Distortion averages around 1/4" per foot and even more at times. This, of course, renders it unfit for multi-color work. Distortion can be controlled a great deal by the use of Naz Dar Stretch Tight which is applied to the screen around the design, or with the use of the new English carbon tissue.

Carbon tissue is used in artgravure and as used in this way there is no distortion, but it requires accuracy and control beyond the practical means of the process trade. For example, the carbon tissue itself must be stored at a certain temperature and degree of humidity. It must be handled, dried, developed and every operation performed at an accurate temperature and humidity and all liquids used in sensitizing, developing, etc., must be kept at a constant temperature. Only in this way can the material be used successfully.

Carbon tissue consists of paper coated uniformly with a film of pigmented gelatin. It usually comes in rolls and may be obtained from most large photographic supply houses. As it comes in rolls or sheet form the gelatin is not light-sensitive.

The first operation is to sensitize the tissue. Cut a piece of the tissue of the size required. In a shallow pan, large enough to take the carbon tissue, place the sensitizing liquid. This sensitizing liquid is ammonium bichromate mixed with water in the proportions of approximately three ounces of bichromate to a gallon of water. While not necessary, it is desirable to neutralize the acid in the bichromate by adding a few drops of ammonia, just enough to turn the solution from an orange to a lemon color. The temperature of this water should not exceed 60° Fahrenheit.

Immerse the tissue in the sensitizing liquid for a period of two minutes. As the tissue becomes limp in the liquid, spread it out flat and be sure that no air bubbles have formed. Have ready a copper plate with an absolutely smooth and clean surface. Before using, dust it lightly with powdered talc, polish with a soft clean cloth and then wipe lightly to remove all surplus talc. Glass may also be used. Remove the tissue from the sensitizer bath and place the tissue with the gelatin side in contact with the copper plate. With a soft rubber or cardboard squeegee, squeegee the tissue carefully with light pressure to remove all air bubbles and surplus water. With dry, absorbent cloths blot the paper and plate so that all surplus liquid is removed. Now place the copper plate in a dark room to dry.

Up to this operation no particular precautions need be observed to keep the tissue protected from light although the operation should not be performed directly under or near a source of artificial or natural light. From this point on, however, precautions must be observed to keep the tissue from contact with light. Work in a dark room under ruby lamps, until the tissue is ready for developing. When the tissue has dried thoroughly on the copper plate, it is ready for exposure. Thorough drying of the tissue is evident when it has curled and become detached from the plate itself. Exposure of the tissue is performed in practically the same manner as any sensitizer used for silk screen process work. A printing frame should be used with the negative placed directly against the gelatin side of the tissue. The paper or back side should be protected by a piece of black cardboard or other means to prevent light from striking it through the paper.

The time of exposure cannot be given here as like all photographic stencils there is a large variable element dependent upon the nature of the light used, the size of the stencil, distance of light from printing frame and the thickness of the negative used. Exposure is complete when the image is clearly and distinctly defined on the paper and there has been a decided change or a darkening of color of the tissue where exposed to light. From one to two minutes of sunlight is usually sufficient.

Have ready a polished copper plate which has previously been waxed and rubbed to a smooth finish. This plate should be prepared beforehand as the wax should be allowed to dry for four or five hours before being used. Also have ready a shallow pan large enough to accommodate the copper plate containing water at a temperature of about 115° Fahrenheit but not exceeding 120° Fahrenheit. Place the copper plate in the bottom of the pan, wax side up. Then place the tissue in the water, gelatin side down and bring the two in contact immediately. Remove from the water and gently squeegee the tissue in all directions so that it adheres in perfect contact with the copper plate. Use just sufficient pressure to remove the surplus water and air bubbles as too much pressure will cause greater distortion. Place this in a dark spot to dry. Replace in the water and move the copper plate back and forth until the paper loosens and becomes detached from the gelatin which remains affixed to the copper plate. When the paper has been removed, continue developing by moving the plate back and forth in the water until the unexposed or design portions have been thoroughly developed or washed out. As development occurs on the surface of the gelatin that was not exposed directly to the light it will be washed partially away.

If a thick stencil is desired, use a longer exposure. If a very thin stencil is desired, use a short exposure as the longer the exposure the less gelatin to be washed away. After developing or washing has been completed, remove the plate and film from the bath. Place it on a level table and place the silk stencil over it. The inside dimensions of the frame on which the silk is stretched should be larger than the copper plate so that the silk will press down on the film with perfect contact. With a soft, clean cloth, gently dab the silk until all portions are adhering firmly to the gelatin and film. Allow to dry. After drying, the copper plate is easily detached from the film which remains affixed to the silk and the stencil is complete.

A photographic film of this nature may usually be removed from the silk by hosing with warm water.

THE ENGLISH CARBON TISSUE METHOD

The special paper required for this method is imported and can be obtained from Geo. Murphy Inc., 57 E. 9th St., New York City, and is known as Number 94.

The first operation is to wax on both sides a sheet of celluloid with the following solution: Break up one cake of hard autotype waxing compound in 24 fluid oz. of pure turpentine by heating. Shake well before using and wax both sides of the celluloid. Place this aside until you are ready to use it. Then take your carbon tissue and submerge it in a cold water bath for 2 minutes or until it is flat enough to turn over and place it back in the bath, face up, for another minute. Drain off any surplus water, and place it face down to the waxed celluloid which has been moistened, squeegee well, being sure that all air bubbles are out.

A clean heavy glass should be placed beneath the celluloid to assure an even surface. On top of the tissue, after wiping dry, place a blotter and on top of this another sheet of heavy glass. Let this set for at least 15 minutes and not more than 20 minutes.

Then take your positive which can be either a line or halftone and place it against the glass in your printing frame, face towards the glass, and against this place your carbon tissue. Affix the light proof pressure backing and expose to your carbon lamp for 7 minutes. The light should be about 28 inches from the frame.

After exposure, the film is returned to cold water, and hot water is added gradually until a temperature of 115° has been reached. This is to wash out the unbaked portions which can be hastened by adding a few drops of ammonia. After the paper has been removed, re-rinse in clean water of 100° and gradually cool until ice cold. Then re-rinse in fresh, clean, cold water.

The tissue is affixed to the silk by placing the celluloid sheet with tissue design on a sheet of heavy glass and on this place the screen, and with warm water, wash the design into the silk. Let this dry, remove the celluloid and it is ready for use.

If film pulls up in spots when stripping the paper off, the cause is usually one of the following: air bubble was present; grain of dirt got under the film; hollow hole in the celluloid or lack of enough squeegeeing.

If the entire film comes up from celluloid with the paper and has a grained, spider-web pattern, the film was too old, mounting water was too warm, or the film was over-exposed.

If film is too thin, developed too rapidly, or paper stripped off too easily, the film was under-exposed.

LABORATORY NOTES

Use distilled water for all film purposes, except in summer when you can chill your films in ordinary cold water, provided a supply of cold distilled water is not handy. By chilling, I mean after development in hot water. Keep oily rags away from celluloid and films because grease is fatal to gelatin work.

Winter Sensitizing Bath—Oct. 15 to May 1

Distilled water .... 100 oz.

Bichromate potassium C. D. .... 2 oz.

Bichromate ammonium C. D. .... 2 oz.

Dissolve bichromates in water. Add 75 grains carbonate soda and 4 oz. wood alcohol. Keep cool in brown bottle or bottle painted black or wrapped in paper.

Summer Sensitizing Bath—May 1 to Oct. 15

Distilled water .... 100 oz.

Bichromate potassium .... 1 oz.

Bichromate ammonium .... 1 oz.

Dissolve above, add 75 gr. carbonate soda, add 2 drams (a dram is ⅛ of a fluid oz.) strong ammonia water 28%; pour 2 oz. wood alcohol into 3 oz. sulphuric ether and add to the bath. Keep cool.

Make a fresh bath every Saturday morning in summer and winter.

CHAPTER XXXII

THE LACQUER PAPER STENCIL

TAKE a piece of thin transparent white tracing paper and tack it to a flat base. Now brush on a coat of Nubian Lacquer* which is made for this purpose, brushing in one direction. Leave it set for an hour and rebrush in the opposite direction. When dry it is ready for use. Place it onto the original drawing with grease. Cut out those portions that are to be printed, place beneath the screen and with a rag saturated with Nubian Thinner rub over the silk. It is well to build up under the design so that the silk lies flat against the design. This is done to prevent wrinkles. Places where the lacquer has run out into the meshes of the silk can be cleaned out by rubbing from the back with thinner. The screen is easily cleaned with any good lacquer thinner.

THE LOOSE FLOP STENCIL

The demand for a cheap medium of stenciling for single short run reproductions has developed the loose flop stencil. For window streamers there is no better medium. The procedure is as follows. On your original design, tack a sheet of Pease natural white tracing paper No. 127 (or any transparent tracing paper). Cut out the portions to be printed, being careful to put aside the centers of letters such as O P B, etc. When the stencil is cut, place the original with the cut out stencil in place on the base,

*Nubian Paint and Varnish Co., Chicago, Ill.

putting the centers in their proper place. Lower the screen and squeegee the paint across the stencil. This will fasten the stencil paper to the silk. The paint must be properly mixed beforehand as it is impossible to wash out this type of stencil.

On the edges of the paper, strips of gummed tape are placed to assure the paper being held rigid and preventing it from slipping. It is a good idea to run the squeegee one way on one sign and in the opposite direction on the next to prevent the paper from shifting.

SANDBLASTING

In sandblasting glass in quantity a means of resisting the pressure of the grains of sand must be placed on the glass to protect those portions that are not to be frosted or sandblasted.

Stencils of various kinds have been used but the best type is screened with a silk screen, either positive or on the back in reverse with a resist of 50% gum arabic and dextrine. To this add 25% of that volume with hide glue which has been heated. This should be in the form of a paste such as any process color. It can be screened onto the glass in the regular way and to eliminate clogging, add a small portion of glycerine. Organdy is the best screen to use and profilm on the wet type that is affixed to the screen by lacquer thinner. When sandblasting is completed, the resist may be washed off with water.

CHAPTER XXXIII

THE PROFILM METHOD

NO method in the making of screens has so revolutionized this branch of the silk screen field as the Profilm method. From crude irregular ragged stencils Profilm has lifted it to a point where it produces sharp distinct plates that when properly handled and made, reproductions are produced that are impossible with any other known method. I will try to cover this method thoroughly with the aid of the producer and distributor of Profilm, Alfred S. Daneman of Dayton, Ohio.

The word Profilm relates to a stencil sheet for use in reproducing of multiple colored designs. One object of Profilm was to provide a stencil sheet which will enable colored designs to be quickly and accurately reproduced at a relatively low cost. A further object was to provide a stencil sheet of such a character that a film, cut away to correspond to the selected portions of the design, may be applied to the screen used in the reproduction of the design. Other objects of Profilm will appear as the stencil sheet is described in detail. (The following numbers 2, 3, 4, 5, and 6, refer in part to a cut of a very simple flag object). (Fig. X-7.)

Fig. 2 represents a design which is to be reproduced.

Fig. 3 shows a stencil sheet with the film cut away to correspond to the selected portions of the design.

Fig. 4 shows a stencil sheet applied to the screen with the backing sheet partially removed.

Fig. 5 shows a stencil sheet with the film cut away to correspond to another portion of the design.

Fig. 6 shows a stencil sheet of Fig. 5 applied to the screen with the backing sheet partially removed.

In these drawings are illustrated one form of stencil

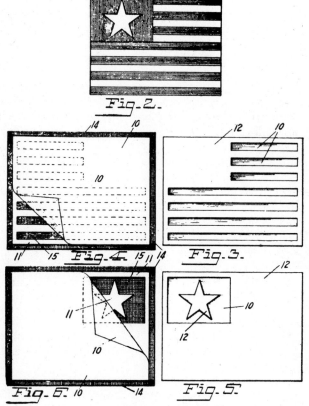

Figure X7.—Flag Object.

sheet embodied in Profilm, together with several steps of the method of using the stencil sheet in the reproduction of multiple colored design.

Profilm comprises a backing sheet of transparent material, having superimposed thereon a film, which is also transparent. The backing sheet and film are of such a character that when thumb tacked or adhesive taped down over the design which is to be reproduced, the colors and outlines of the design will be perfectly visible through the stencil sheet. In using the stencil sheet in the reproduction of a design, it is superimposed over the design and secured in fixed relation thereto with the film side up. Those portions of the film, that lie above and correspond to those portions of the design, which are of one color, are then cut away by means of a pictorial, or lithographic, flat edged stencil knife, or any tool that can be satisfactorily handled by a stencil cutter. That portion of the film which is being cut away is removed from the backing sheet by peeling. The backing sheet is not cut through but remains integral, and thus forms a continuous support for those parts of the film which are not removed, and maintains the same in their proper relative positions.

In Fig. 2 of the drawing is illustrated a simple design of a flag, which is to be reproduced, and Fig. 3 shows the stencil sheet with the film cut away to correspond to one set of stripes on the flag, all of which are one color. The stencil sheet, with the film thus cut away to provide the same with openings corresponding to the selected portions of the design, is then placed upon the screen which is used in the reproduction of the design.

This screen ordinarily comprises a rectangular frame of a light wood, sturdily built, over which is stretched and tacked a sheet of fine mesh fabric, preferably silk. The stencil sheet is then placed on the fabric of the screen with the film in contact therewith, and is caused to adhere to the fabric of the screen with a heated electric iron. After the Profilm stencil sheet has been made to adhere to the silk mesh, the backing sheet, shown as No. 10 in Fig. X-7, is peeled off, described in Fig. 4, thus leaving the film upon the screen. The screen is then placed over the sheet of cardboard, or whatever type of material you are printing on, and on which the reproduction is to be made, and the color applied through the openings in the film on the screen by means of a squeegee. It will be obvious that the film will prevent the color from coming in contact with any part of the sheet other than those portions which are in line with the openings in the film, and in this manner, the material is provided with the first color of the design.

After this first color has been applied to a number of sheets corresponding to the number of reproductions it is desired to make, which may run into the thousands, the screen is cleansed by washing with a solvent, which will soften the film and permit it to be removed, using the same screen over and over.

A second stencil sheet of Profilm is then superimposed upon the design, exactly as outlined in the first instance, and the film is cut away to provide openings throughout, corresponding to those parts of the design which are of a second color. In Fig. 5, I have shown the film cut to correspond to the field of the flag, and it will be noted that the film is cut completely away on all sides of the star, which is arranged in the field, but the film corresponding to the star adheres firmly to its backing sheet, and is thus held in its proper position with relation to the other parts of the film. This second stencil sheet is then applied to the screen in the aforesaid manner, described as the first stencil sheet was applied thereto, in exactly the same position occupied by the first stencil sheet, spoken of as in register.

After the film has been caused to adhere to the screen, the backing sheet is removed and the screen is then superimposed over the sheets on which the first color has been reproduced, care being taken to see that the screen occupies exactly the same perfect registration that it occupied in the first instance, so that the openings in the film through which the second color is to be applied, will be in proper relations to those portions of the film sheet to which the first color has been applied.

After the second color has been applied to all the sheets, or material on which you are printing, the screen may again be cleansed and the operation repeated as often as it is necessary to provide the reproductions with all the colors of the design. (It will be obvious, of course, that instead of using a single screen, and cleansing the same, after the application of each color, a plurality of separate screens may be employed, speeding up the completion of the job. Production can be started on completion of the very first stencil, the remaining stencils can be in the process of preparation while the first stencil is in action in the producing room.)

A master copy approved is the very beginning of any process printing job. If your master copy has been designed on more or less flimsy paper, mount it on fairly stiff, thin cardboard of the same dimensions as the stock you are going to reproduce on, the four sides of which are absolutely square. The reason of this absolute precision is for registration purposes, which are so very vital in multiple colored work.

CUTTING A PROFILM STENCIL

Not a great amount of skill is required to cut a good stencil. An experienced stencil cutter can cut stencils, representing a complete design of seven colors, that is to be reproduced and of more or less intricate designs, in from eight to ten hours. Just visualize what this speed, at little cost, and at the same time producing a most marvelous result in an engraved like manner, means to the producers of such work as compared to the preparation of color printing and lithographing methods.

If you are, for instance, going to prepare stencils for a five color design, cut four pieces of Profilm to size of master copy you are going to reproduce. Place a permanent visible registration mark in each corner of your master copy for precise future registration purposes and place one piece of your Profilm over the master copy, film side up, as shown in Fig. X-8. You can see the master copy through the Profilm, distinguishing one color from the other easily. Thumb tack or adhesive tape this piece of Profilm to the master copy securely, as shown in

Figure X8.—Correct Way of Cutting Stencil.

Fig. X-8, so the Profilm *cannot move one way or the other* on the master copy during the cutting of the stencil. With a lithographer's needle or a pictorial stencil knife, mark the Profilm, which is attached on top of the master copy, film side up, to absolutely correspond with the four registration marks you placed in the four corners of the master copy.

The reason for marking Profilm to correspond to the markings on the master copy, is because after you have cut your first stencil in Profilm, you are going to release this piece of Profilm from the original copy, and you must have both the original and the Profilm stencil of the first color marked to correspond perfectly, because of future operations.

Use an ordinary stylus, pictorial, flat edged knife, to cut out your design—that is to say, cut in a tracing manner through the film (*to* its backing sheet) and peel the film from the backing sheet. All places where you are peeling the film from its backing sheet will become openings on the screen, through which the paint, when pressed through with a squeegee, produces the design after the film has been attached to the screen. If you happen to cut completely through the backing sheet, here or there, which you will no doubt do at first, you have not impaired your stencil. But, if you cut completely through surrounding a center, your center will fall out. The film is firmly attached to its backing sheet for the purpose of holding all details in your stencil in perfect position, corresponding to your master copy, until such time as you transfer the film to the screen, and remove its backing sheet, as shown in Fig. X-8.

The reason for cutting only four pieces of Profilm to size of master copy to produce a five color job, is that possibly one color of the print showing in your master copy will take form by the color of the material itself on which you are printing, thereby eliminating one complete color run.

In cutting stencils for a multiple colored job, always remember to lap the edge of one color over the other. The width of the lap is determined by the type of design you are working on, and always remember to run dark colors over light.

ATTACHING PROFILM TO SCREEN IN REGISTER

As the first color of your master copy has been cut into Profilm, causing a stencil to be formed, you are now ready to attach the stencil to your screen over your master copy in perfect registration. Raise your screen, place

Build-up under screen with cardboard which should be cut smaller than frame to secure perfect contact between silk and cut stencil which is lying film side up on build-up.

Figure X9.—Procedure for Perfect Contact Between Stencil and Silk.

your master copy, (which has the same dimensions as material you are printing on as described in the foregoing, as being on fairly stiff cardboard, the four sides of which are absolutely square), under the screen, and set the master copy so that it will take the position on the screen desired; then fasten down your two "L" shaped corner markers, being very careful to see that your master copy fits in them straight.

(The following description of registration applies to a simple design involving few colors with little tie-up.)

Replace the first color stencil you intend to run over the master copy, after following above instructions—

lining up the four marks on the stencil to the four marks on the master copy—drop your screen carefully, being sure that you do not move the stencil.

After you are sure you have the Profilm stencil in perfect registration with the master copy, and the screen

Figure X10.—Proper Method of Using Iron.

resting on it, take a hot electric iron and touch five or six spots with the pointed edge of the iron through the silk to the face of the Profilm, which is underneath the silk. The touching of the electric iron will attach the stencil to your screen sufficiently to allow you to draw out the master copy, however keeping the stencil in perfect register on the screen although only partially attached. Insert in its place, one or two heavy pieces of cardboard, cut to a size that will come within the frame of your screen underneath, (known as a build-up). When placing the screen, flat side down over these pieces of cardboard, neither of the four edges of which will touch the frame of your screen, the purpose is that when you push down on the frame of the screen, the cardboard lying underneath will push the silk up a trifle, giving you perfect surface contact between the Profilm stencil and the silk, all of which is described in Fig. X-9. Cut one or two pieces of ordinary light

Figure X11.—Peeling Off Backing Paper.

weight wrapping paper to a size that will come within the frame of your screen, and after you have followed the instructions given, take the electric iron, fairly hot, and iron on top of the paper, which is now lying in the screen, under which is your Profilm stencil, as illustrated in Fig. X-10. Turn your screen over, as described in Fig. X-11, wait a few seconds, then start from any one of the four corners and peel off the backing paper. In peeling off the backing sheet, do it slowly and watch carefully to be sure that in removing the backing sheet, you are not removing some of the detail, which did not happen to adhere to the screen with the first ironing.

In the event there is some detail that is coming off with the backing sheet, allow your backing paper to fall back in its original position, turn the screen over again, as illustrated in Fig. X-10, take your electric iron and iron these various spots again; then remove the backing sheet, place the screen down in the same position, as shown in Fig. X-10, and iron again. Be sure you are ironing on the paper, and not directly on the silk, and remember, the last time you iron, the backing sheet has been removed. This last ironing is to insure perfect adhesion of your film with all its detail to the screen.

This first color Profilm stencil is now in perfect registration on your screen with your master copy and your stops or registration marks attached to your process base. Now, the stock on which you are going to do your printing, or reproducing, is of course of the same size as the cardboard mounting upon which is attached your master copy; therefore, the picture, the first color stencil of which is now attached to your screen, will print in perfect position on whatever stock you are going to use. Every succeeding color operation is performed exactly as the very first color described in detail herein.

ADDITIONAL REGISTRATION INSTRUCTIONS ON A DESIGN OF MANY COLORS AND DETAILED TIE-UP

A tracing should be used for this method of registration as a guide, to register the stencils on the screen as they are needed. This is done by laying the screen over the master copy and tracing that part of the stencil you desire to run first. Having this completed, the screen is placed in an upright position so that the stencil can be held in proper register (according to the tracing on the silk) while an electric iron is used on the opposite side of the screen to fasten the four corners of the stencil. This will hold the stencil in register so that you can place the screen on a proper ironing base, and the foregoing described ironing procedure is followed as described in Fig. X-10. The stencils for the colors to follow are registered in a like manner, according to the tracings on the silk. Any small openings between the registered stencils on the screen are easily sealed with lacquer filler. A stencil is framed in a like manner by sealing the open spaces between the outside of the stencil and the frame, or any other portion that is not to be used in printing.

PERFECT REGISTER

One of the most essential items in the equipment to produce perfectly registered silk screen method printing is a process table, which, however, is nothing more than a strong, well braced table, 36 to 40″ high. A very important part connected with this table is its base, the unevenness of which will cause considerable trouble. Well seasoned, kiln dried lumber should be used in the construction of a process table. The top should be perfectly smooth, and even, and of a laminated construction. An efficient size of your table would constitute a sized top that would allow you to attach your screen unit of most any size thereon, and still have plenty of room for your raw stock on which you are printing, your paint, and various other items that you may need during the printing of a job; for instance, materials for thinning out the color you are working within the frame while printing, as at times from being worked back and forth, your color may become a little too thick and heavy, and therefore it is necessary to thin it out to its original consistency for efficient and smooth operations.

FRAME CONSTRUCTIONS FOR SCREENS

Constructions for frames, upon which you attach your silk or organdy, and through which you will print, are many. I am only going to give you two types, both of which are exceedingly simple to construct and are in use generally. In building any size frame, to fit the particular job you intend to produce, always have a four to six inch margin at the top and bottom of the design on the screen attached to the frame and three or four inches on the sides.

The margin at the bottom, or the end closest to the operator, is where the bulk of your color is resting during the process of operation. The least expensive method of constructing a frame is to cut your lumber out of well seasoned, light weight, but sturdy material—cut to the size required, miter at the corners, fasten with steel clips, and possibly you may reinforce the corners with an "L" shaped piece of metal screwed into the frame. Upon this frame, stretch and tack your silk or organdy—the tacks should be placed a half-inch apart.

Another type of frame is known in the industry as a floating bar frame. The bars within the frame are adjustable by tie-bolts.

TACKING ON SILK

Always start to tack the silk at the upper or lower edge of the frame. (*Be careful to see that the threads of your silk run perfectly parallel with your frame*), either the right or left side, leaving one end and one side loose, enabling you to grasp the loose end for tightening down to the frame with one hand while you are tacking with the other. Stretch the silk over the frame in a drum-like manner, using your own judgment as you progress along in the stretching as to which direction and how strenuously you will pull while tacking, as you must be very careful to have absolutely no wrinkles. After the above is completed, bathe your screen in cold water, and allow it to dry. This will draw your silk even tighter over your frame.

Fasten your wooden frame screen to your base with hinges, and as hinges might have a certain amount of give and play, the action will be detrimental in keeping a perfect register; therefore, a peg inserted in the frame with a blunt edge to correspond and fit into a hole in the process base will be the means of locking the frame to keep perfect register with the top of the table, thereby assuring absolute rigidity and perfect alignment at all times.

The above outfit, as described, is for printing on more or less flat materials, such as cardboard, wood, glass, cloth, metal, etc. However, one of the greatest advantages of the silk screen paint process method of printing is the fact that it will enable you to print on irregular and odd shaped commodities. All that is necessary to efficiently perform the printing on odd shaped commodities, is to build the frame to fit the article.

REMOVING A PROFILM STENCIL FROM THE SCREEN

In order to remove a Profilm stencil completely from the screen, place a heavy woolen cloth, inside the frame, and saturate this cloth with genuine wood alcohol. Let it soak 15 or 20 minutes, and then rub briskly with the same woolen cloth, well saturated with wood alcohol, and your Profilm stencil will drop off the screen. A Profilm stencil, properly ironed on to the screen, will never cause any difficulty in removing. However, if it has not been properly attached to the screen, (that is to say, an iron that was much too hot, or a greasy screen was used, or a screen that had invisible at the time to the naked eye, paint dried and immeshed in the silk), we can supply a powdered material mixed 40% in weight of the powder to 60% in weight of hot water that will positively, when poured onto the screen quickly, and rinsed quickly with cold water, remove all signs of mesh clog. However, I am going to repeat that if a Profilm stencil is properly attached to the screen, nothing will be necessary in removing it completely but wood alcohol.

THICKNESS OF PROFILM

A Profilm stencil on the screen is very thin, at the same time, very tough, and does not develop pin holes at any time, regardless of the length of the run; therefore, a thin Profilm stencil will naturally deposit a very thin print of color in making up the design, which, of course, is a great advantage, both in the savings of paint, and in the final results obtained. However, if a heavy raised effect is desired, a heavier Profilm can be made to obtain the desired results. Consistency of color used plays a very important part in results described here.

TROUBLES THAT MAY DEVELOP

Screen clogging seems to be one of the paramount difficulties. This can be minimized, however, by using process colors that are manufactured by reputable paint concerns. Lint from your cardboard, or material upon which the screen is continually raised and lowered during the running of a job, may cause some clogging, due to the screen picking up, over a period of time, lint or other particles, thereby clogging the small little mesh openings; also improper pressure on the squeegee and improper cleaning of a screen will cause clogging.

You are cautioned to keep your screens absolutely open and clean, not only in the open part of the stencil through which you are printing, but also in that part of the stencil where your Profilm is attached to the silk, because when you remove a Profilm stencil from the screen to be supplied by another stencil of entirely different design, it is obvious that your screen in its entirety should be open and clean, as you do not know where the open spots on your new stencil will happen to be placed on the screen for the run of a new job. Kerosene, gasoline, or benzine, are all very good for cleaning silk mesh. Improper consistency of paint, even of good quality, will cause trouble in the screen during the process of printing. Dull squeegees will cause trouble, improper contact between the screen on which is attached the stencil, and the material on which you are printing, would also cause some difficulty.

ADDITIONAL INFORMATION ON FRAMING SCREENS OR CLOSING ALL OPEN SPACES THROUGH WHICH YOU DO NOT WISH TO PRINT

The open spaces on your screen between the edge of your stencil, and the edges of your wooden frame, should be properly closed in the following manner: seal these openings with lacquer filler, preferable squeegeed on; however, they can be closed up by brushing lacquer filler, thereby filling the open spaces through which you do not care to have the color come in contact with the stock on which you are printing. If these openings are not properly closed, you will encounter untold difficulty during a run that will delay you unnecessarily; in fact, every reason for developing troubles can be eliminated by careful practice of the operators. Closing open spaces around stencils on the screen, between the stencil and the frame, is done on the bottom or flat side of the screen. However, there is still another method, that of sealing open spaces by using adhesive paper tape. This is done inside of the screen.

In cutting your Profilm to size, proper measurements of master copy, that is, before you start to cut your first stencil of any job, see that these various pieces of Profilm to be used, and from which you will make your stencils, are cut to come within at least one and a half inches from the edges of your frame on the silk. This will enable you easy access to the very edges of your stencil when attaching to the screen with your iron.

SILK

I wish to call my readers' particular attention to one of the extremely important parts Profilm plays in producing fine detail and sharp edges through a more or less coarse mesh. It is a well established fact that you cannot paint a straight edged line across a screen, inasmuch as the results are bound to take the shape of what we term a "saw tooth edge." This poor result is not caused by the ability of the operator, who is still using the old method of "cutting in" the design on the screen by hand, but is caused by the paint jumping the mesh holes as he draws his brush across the silk; in other words, you cannot make paint hold in open spaces. This great difficulty (and it is a great difficulty, inasmuch as the results of a process job are continually compared with lithographed or printed results by the purchaser), will be the so-called "saw tooth edge" produced in effect by "cutting in" on the screen by hand, a method which has been supplanted almost entirely by Profilm, inasmuch as the above mentioned detrimental effect is completely removed by its use when applied to the screen as a stencil.

The use of Profilm will not only produce engraved, sharp effects, but will also eliminate high priced silk, inasmuch as you can get just as fine and sharp a line through coarse silk or organdy, as you can obtain with the finest mesh that you are able to purchase for silk screen paint process printing; therefore, Profilm gives you the desired result, and at the same time, eliminates the use of high priced silk.

CHAPTER XXXIV

NU-FILM METHOD

THE instructions contained in the following pages make it possible for either the novice or the expert to produce a perfect screen with Nu-Film. All the operations are vital to the finished screen. The instructions are practical and are based upon the experiences of the best silk screen operators in the country.

Cutting Tools:

Knife—A fine stencil cutting knife should be used. The knife can be kept in good cutting condition by sharpening on a piece of Hard Arkansas Oil Stone, using a little kerosene rather than machine oil.

Compass—A pair of dividers make a fine compass when one side is sharpened to the same kind of a cutting edge as the knife.

Rulers—An assortment of brass or steel rulers are indispensable.

Adhesive Tape—A roll of adhesive tape sold under the trade name of Scotch Tape is a necessity.

HOW TO USE NU-FILM

Thumb tack original sketch or lay-out sheet to either a drawing board or work table. (A drawing board will be found to have many advantages over a work table as the operator can turn it at will, also sit in a more comfortable position during the cutting operation.)

In pencil or ink draw a cross in each of the four corners

of the original sketch to facilitate replacing Nu-Film in exact registration.

Cut a piece the size of the original sketch for each color. With scotch tape fasten the Nu-Film to the original

FIG. 1. Nu-Film fastened to original sketch with Scotch tape, and operator in process of cutting same

sketch. Use enough tape so that the Nu-Film is down tight and will not shift. Nu-Film may also be temporarily held with wax. We are ready for cutting.

Cutting:

Since Nu-Film is a construction of a thin specially prepared film laminated to a sheet of translucent paper, the paper acting only as a temporary carrier of the film until such time as the transfer to the silk is made, after which the paper is removed. The idea is to cut through the film only and not through the backing paper.

The order in which the colors are to be processed is the same when working with Nu-Film as with any other method. After deciding which color is going to be run first, you proceed to cut a stencil corresponding with that color—allowing sufficient overlap of one color over the other to take care of proper registration.

In a tracing manner using the fine stencil knife, cut through the Nu-Film to the backing paper. Use light pressure in cutting as bearing down heavy will cause cutting of the backing paper. (An hour or so of practice

FIG. 2. Stripping Nu-Film from the cut portions. (Note that the knife cuts have been carried beyond the corners of the lettering.)

cutting should be sufficient to get the feel of it.) After cutting has been completed, strip out all Nu-Film from portion of the design which is to appear open on the screen. Now remove cut Nu-Film for color No. 1 and roll up with film surface outside. Repeat the same operation for each remaining color.

Adhering Nu-Film to the Screen:

Prepare a screen. Be sure it is clean and that oil or kerosene residue has been removed by washing with either turpentine or lacquer thinner. **If new silk is used, wash well with water to remove the sizing.**

In all the larger open spaces from which Nu-Film has been stripped, cut a slit through the backing paper. The purpose of this is to allow the escape of air during the adhering operation.

Place screen in hinges on the printing table. Make ready by setting register guides in the usual manner. Place lay-out sheet in register and bring down screen so that the silk is in contact with the lay-out sheet. Be sure that

FIG. 3. Adhering Nu-Film. (Note that operator wets a small portion of the screen.)

contact is good. If contact is poor, build up by using a piece of cardboard under the lay-out sheet. Fit back Nu-Film for color No. 1 to the original position in which it was cut and fasten with scotch tape.

Examine Nu-Film stencil to make sure that no small pieces have been left in the cut portions.

Take two pieces of rag, one large and one small, (preferably cotton rags of the type of shirts or underwear. Do not use cheesecloth or similar rags as difficulty will be encountered in judging the amount of liquid applied.) The large one, roll up in a loose ball. Wet the small rag with adhering liquid. Hold the wet rag in one hand and the dry one in the other. Wet a small portion of the screen by taking a single stroke and dry it immediately with dry rag using a rubbing motion. You will note when this has been done that adhesion was instant. Continue in the same manner until the entire film has been adhered, wetting the small rag as often as is necessary. In adhering always start from one side of the screen and continue in the same direction to avoid wrinkles.

When the entire piece of Nu-Film has been adhered,

FIG. 4. Dry immediately with a light rubbing motion. Sufficient rubbing must be done with the dry rag so that adhering liquid is completely evaporated.

take a thin straight-edge or ruler, slip it under the Nu-Film and free the screen from the lay-out sheet by loosening the scotch tape. Remove the screen from the hinges and lay it on the table backing paper side up. Allow to dry about 10 minutes.

Removing Backing Paper:

Start in any one of the four corners and slowly peel backing paper off. Peel backing paper so that you can at all times see the Nu-Film in order to prevent tearing any portion of it that was not well adhered. Should any portion of it be improperly adhered, do not remove the backing paper, but turn screen over again and by wetting and drying that portion, proper adhesion will be accomplished.

When the backing paper has been completely removed, if there still are some loose places, turn screen with

FIG. 5. Removing backing paper

Nu-Film side up, wet rag with adhering liquid and dampen the loose part from the under side of the screen and pat down from the Nu-Film side with your finger. This will complete adhesion.

Fill in with lacquer or mask with paper the open silk, bordering the Nu-Film. You are now ready for printing.

Removal of Nu-Film from the Silk:

The simplicity of this is another of the outstanding features of Nu-Film.

Take a sheet of wrapping or similar paper. It must be smooth. Lay this paper on a flat table, place screen on top of paper so that Nu-Film is in contact with it. Take a good sized rag and soak it well with our super film remover. Wash over the Nu-Film portions of the screen keeping the rag well saturated. After a few moments take hold of the paper and pull it away from the silk and it will take all the Nu-Film with it. Take a couple of clean rags and wet them with our remover and wash the silk well from both sides at the same time. Dry the silk with a dry rag and it will be clean.

Points and Suggestions:

Use a sharp knife for cutting.

Use a clean screen.

Examine Nu-Film before adhering to make sure it is properly cut.

Slit the backing paper in all the larger openings to allow the escape of air during adhering.

Adhere Nu-Film in register on the printing table to insure good register.

In adhering start from one end of the screen and continue in one direction to avoid wrinkles.

Do not oversoak Nu-Film with adhering liquid as this will spoil the sharp edge. Follow adhering instructions carefully.

Be sure Nu-Film is properly adhered before removing the backing paper.

Perfect adhering is the result of good contact between the silk and the Nu-Film.

Your reward for a little extra effort, will be a far superior job.

CHAPTER XXXV

GLASS SIGNS, ETCHING AND BACK-UP

SINCE the first edition of Silk Screen Methods of Reproduction, considerable progress has been made in process manufacture of glass signs. The offset Swedish printing method has been entirely discontinued on flat surface glass work because it was too costly, and the screen has replaced it by cutting etching costs 75%. Another new achievement was the adoption of chemical gold solution, eliminating gold leaf gilding. The improvements save fifty percent in costs and also are of greater durability. A few more additions in gilding worth mentioning are: copper, which gives you a red gold color which resembles the new flesh color glass. Lighter shades are produced by adding a trace of platinum or palladium. Gun metal finishes are produced by a flow of lead nitrate in solution. Roman gold or dark gold is produced by a thin solution of gold and double coated with copper. Light gold can be made by a thin coat of transparent silver and double coated with genuine gold chloride solution; or better than that would be the most durable solution, gold chloride and a trade of platinum, which is termed as an everlasting mirror.

The formula of acid resist for glass etching will not be mentioned, due to fire hazards in its manufacture, so we suggest getting a supply ready mixed. For the average five-minute acid etch, one coat of resist is sufficient. For deep etching we suggest two coats of acid resist, and for

194

a depth of ⅛″ or more, we advise three screenings which will resist acid without danger of fuming for over seven hours. The hydrofluoric acid can be purchased in various strengths, 48, 52 and 60. The most commonly used is 52%, to which fifty percent water is added. This proportion makes a perfect mixture. A flat etch, or commonly called, mat finish is laid flat in an acid tank, etching after cleaned and brushed for six minutes, after which it is drained and washed. The resist is washed off with hot water or dipped in a naphtha tank and cleaned with sawdust, and afterwards washed with whiting and ammonia water and then rinsed.

The deep etch imitation chipping is set in acid tank upside down so that the silicate may drop out, forming irregular designs. Four pegs will be necessary to hoist the glass from touching the bottom of tank; a better and more satisfactory etch may be gotten by this method.

After every batch of glass is etched, an addition of stronger acid must be added. The acid tanks should be made of ¼″ acid-resisting lead, the corners folded instead of cutting to eliminate soldering. The tanks should be designed for covers because the gas of hydrofluoric acid escapes very readily, which weakens the solution. After the day's work or idle time, the covers are let down to preserve the strength of your etching acid, which also prevents the fumes escaping and doing much damage to the surface of all glass that it may get in contact with. A well ventilated room with a 30″ exhaust fan is necessary; all precaution must be used not to inhale the fumes, as they are very dangerous. Heavy duty rubber acid gloves should be used for handling glass while putting in or taking articles from the acid tank.

When these operations are completed, washing and then gilding is considered the next step. The gilding table is similar to that used by mirror manufacturers. The table should be perfectly level, covered with heavy cotton cloth with at least five coverings to absorb moisture and collect the surplus water poured off the glass when gilded. The table is heated to about 120 degrees F. and in most cases heated by a series of steam pipes four inches apart, covered with soapstone or slate and also cotton covering.

The most commonly used silver for pouring is the tartaric acid solution, for which we will give a complete formula. The first operation is called scratch polishing. This is done either by a hand block felt pad or by a rough wheel. All fine hair line scratches and rubs are polished out, then washed clean. A tinning solution is made to sensitize the glass for silver. To one gallon of distilled water, 5 grains of Tin Muriate A.R. is dissolved and poured on clean (while wet) glass, and then rinsed with distilled water. Now we are ready for the silvering.

Mix 8 oz. of silver nitrate C.P. and ¾ gal. distilled water. Dissolve and stir with a glass rod. Then add 10 oz. of ammonium hydroxide, 28% C.P. The solution will be turbid. Then drop by drop of ammonium is added until the solution clears. This is what we term as Solution #1.

To one gallon of distilled water, 4 oz. of tartaric acid granulated is dissolved. When completed this is solution #2.

> 1 pt. of distilled water
> 3 oz. of Solution 1
> 3 oz. of Solution 2

Mix thoroughly and pour on glass, and in ten minutes a precipitated silver in metallic form will adhere to the glass.

Rinse with common water and dry. For a bright edge of silver around design or lettering, this can be arranged by cutting a screen to match. The paint for this should be neutral. The varnish in this, black preferably, should not contain rosinic acid because it may be injurious to the silver. After the color is dry, it may be brushed or dipped in a weak solution of water and nitric acid and the surplus silver will be removed, then rinsed and dried. We are now ready for final operations, which are the background colors. We recommend a chemically pure color with as little in earths as possible.

A good gold formula is given in detail.

Solution #1.—1 oz. of gold chloride to
1 gal. of distilled water

Solution #2.—2 oz. of potassium hydroxide A.R.
1 gal. of distilled water

Solution #3.—½ pt. of distilled water
½ pt. of #40 S.D. alcohol
5 grams of sucrose
2 drops of glycerine
5 grams of formaldehyde

To 16 oz. of number (1) solution add 112 oz. of solution (2). This makes 1 gal. of liquid gold ready which should be mixed three hours in advance for aging. We recommend that it should be used before two weeks as it spoils with age.

The tinning is required like that of silver. After rinsing, a priming coat of weak silver nitrate solution is poured and rinsed. Then to 1 pt. of gold solution ready mixed, after proper aging, add one full eye dropper of Solution #3, mixed by pouring back and forth several times, and then pour on glass. A cold table may be used, the only difference being that the amount of gold precipitation does not compare with that of a hot table. A fairly solid film of gold will be deposited in about eight minutes, then it should be properly rinsed and a coat of tartaric acid solution of silver should be deposited, which will be opaque when completed.

To be successful in silvering, proper proportions in the ingredients must be exercised. The working of the solutions must be exercised and watched with care. Should there be no immediate deposit, it can be assured that the proportions were not accurate. We would advise never to use a chamois skin for drying the excess surplus liquid after the completion of either gold or silver gilding. Years of experience have taught us that a chemical reaction takes place which mottles the reflection.

A transparent mirror has been used in advertising and other mediums, so we will give you the following formula. A hot table is not necessary. The method, if properly used, will be very durable.

Stock solution

(1) Nitrate of silver............ 4 oz.
     Distilled water ....60 oz.

(2) Potassium hydroxide .... 4 oz.
     Distilled water ....60 oz.

(3) Ammonium hydroxide, drop by
        drop to clear the above mixture

(4) Sucrose or cane sugar........ 1 oz.
     C.P. sulphuric acid.........5 drops
     Pure alcohol ....½ oz.

Always remember four oz. of solution to a square foot of glass, so in mixing the above solution, a pitcher that will carry sufficient liquid should be used. The gilding takes place immediately, and in order to avoid spotting the liquid must be poured at once. Estimate the amount of solution needed. Then mix #1, #2 and #3. This mixture when cleared with number three is considered ready to pour by adding 10% of solution #4. It will take considerable time and effort to understand the proper action, to make a good transparent mirror, so don't be discouraged, if you should fail the first or second time. The stock solution will keep in a closed bottle, but do not attempt to save the mixed solutions #1, #2 and #3.

They are dangerous, especially in a hot room or standing on a hot gilding table.

The first covering will be transparent. Another coat can be poured, and if a quick opaque mirror is wanted, the third coat can be poured and then shellacked when dry. The method has proven to stand up very well. A coat of Egyptian asphaltum thinned with toluol, is a very good backing; shellac is not necessary in this case.

A few points to be remembered in handling glass after it has been roughed: Be careful that you do not touch the surface to be silvered with your hands; if you do, it will bear a mark and the solution will not deposit properly. The glass should be handled by the edge so no contact with the hands will be made. Double coating is not necessary. An opaque deposit can be precipitated on the first pouring. About four ounces of liquid solution is ample for each square foot of silver.

All possible care must be taken in keeping measuring glass pitchers and bottles so that they are at all times chemically free from foreign matter. The best way to keep them clean is to pour a dilute solution of aque regia or hydrochloric acid, rinsing with water, then whiting and ammonia for final wash. Keep them upside down while not in use. It is not necessary to filter the solutions if care is taken in all operations. The purity of your distilled water may be tested by adding a few drops of silver nitrate in water, and if it becomes cloudy, the water is not pure.

To remove silver or gold stains from your hands or clothes, wash with a dilute solution of 1 part of sodium cyanide to 50 parts of common water. After stain disappears, wash immediately with water, so no trace of cyanide may remain; should be kept away from open sores, for it is very poisonous. Keep in bottle and label with large letters (Poison) so you may detect it at a glance.

A white acid etch may be fumed on glass by the following process:

    Water 22%
    Ammonium biflouride 38%
    Sodium flouride 20%
    White syrup 10%
    Hydrofluoric acid 10%

This formula will white acid-etch in 2 minutes. The solution must be agitated to avoid spotting. Rinse immediately in warm water so that no fuming will occur. The fuming or white acid etch will be most effective in a warm well ventilated room. We suggest the above mixtures be made at least two days in advance, so that all ingredients will amalgamate properly.

COPPER ELECTROPLATED SCREENS

In many industries especially where vitreous or Ceramics are used, a strong type of screen is necessary. It is possible to make a copper screen by first taking a piece of copper mesh wire, thoroughly cleaning and placing the design or portion to be printed on this wire with a resist. Either shellac or lacquer may be used. It is then coated with the resist on the opposite side over the same pattern or design. It is then put into the electro plating tank which will put a coating of thin copper over all except the resist. If lacquer is used the resist is removed with acetone, and if shellac is used the resist is removed with alcohol.

CHAPTER XXXVI

FLOCK AND FLOCK FINISHES

THIS interesting, popular and profitable means of placing designs etc., on most surfaces with a cloth like fabric is by no means new, but has recently been revived with many new uses. "Flock" is a term applied to short thread-like fibres of cotton, wool or rayon and

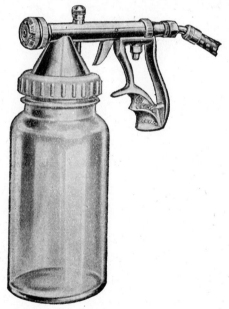

FIG. 1. Type of Spray Gun Used for Flocking

may be dyed to any color or shade. It is applied to the surface by either spray gun, silk screen or hand method. The flock is then blown or dropped on the wet paint or adhesive. If a special high nap is desired on flexible sur-

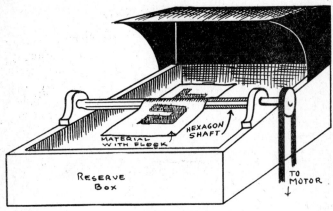

FIG. 2.

faces, it is placed on a bumper or spanker bar which creates a static, thereby causing the flock to stand on end.

On silk screen where a heavy deposit is desired, a thicker type of material on the stencil is necessary. This will place a heavier deposit of adhesive on the material, thereby causing a thicker, heavier flock.

The color or design to be flocked is screened directly on the fabric or surface with a synthetic or varnish type of paint. While the color is still wet, place the flock on this wet paint with a spray gun. (See Fig. 1.) It may also be dropped from a strainer, a flour strainer being ideal. Before the color has a chance to set, rub the material over a bumper or spanker bar. (See Fig. 2.) Better adhesion to fabrics may be obtained by stretching the fabric before stenciling.

When using flock on displays, etc., where many different colors are desired, all colors are screened with the regular flat type of poster paint. When this is dry, silk screen over the entire surface to be flocked, a coating of a heavy varnish or transparent base and put a light grey

FIG. 3.   Cloth Coat Finished by Flocking Process

or white flock over this. The bottom or poster colors will show through and give the effect of the flock being colored.

Where flock is to be used on large surfaces, such as caskets, interior of automobiles, window backgrounds, etc., the adhesive must be applied with a spray gun, the color in this case being thinned with varnish. Flock may be reclaimed with a vacuum cleaner or a special flocking booth. When adhering flock to porous surfaces such as cardboard, wood, concrete, etc., the surface must first be primed or coated, as the paint otherwise would soak into the surface. Flock is being applied efficiently to all types of caskets, interiors of automobile trunks and glove compartments, bottom of dishes, ornaments, telephones, inside of cameras, on pennants, athletic goods, books, furniture, radio interiors, window backgrounds, displays, etc.

Other materials may be used instead of flock, such as beads, sawdust, powdered leather, sand, metallics, etc.

FLOCKING ON CLOTH AND YARD GOODS

This is a process whereby expensive woven patterns can be imitated with flock on the cloth. The machine (see Fig. 4), for this consists of two cylinders or rollers

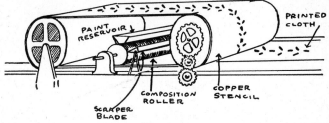

Fig. 4

set parallel to each other. Around these run a copper stencil on which the patterns have been cut out, forming an endless belt. Between these is a composition or rubber roller. On top of this is the paint reservoir and slightly to one side and riding against the roller is the scraper blade. When the machine is in operation, the upper portion of the stencil moves toward the back, the lower stretch toward the front or in the same direction that the cloth runs. The cloth being printed, passes under the bottom of the copper stencil and the paint being forced through the openings will be deposited on the cloth. It then goes to the flocking chamber which puts flock on both sides of the cloth. It is then festooned and placed in the drying room and force dried. Heat should be around 140 degrees. When dry, it is brushed and is ready to be rolled. This same unit can be used to print patterns and designs on the cloth with lacquers and dyes that will not require flock.

CLEANING AND DEGREASING COPPER OR BRONZE

Soak the screen for 30 minutes in a cold solution of

sodium metasilicate. It is then swabbed with a 40%
Baume solution of ferric chloride for a minute and then
washed in clear water. It is again soaked and washed in
sodium metasilicate solution.

CHAPTER XXXVII

TWENTY-FOUR SHEET POSTER

T WENTY-FOUR Sheet Poster, all or part, are being processed because in many instances there have been times when it was impossible to accept orders for short runs as the cost of lithographic plates was prohibitive.

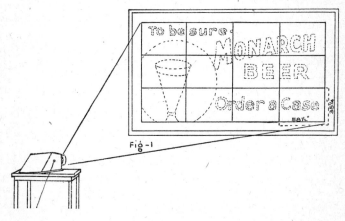

Fig-1

With silk screen, runs up to 100 or more, even 10 or 12 are economical. Even where there are long runs which are lithographed, where imprints, local conditions, etc., require names, prices, etc., only certain portions may be processed. This is particularly true where dealers' names are to be imprinted. The 24 sheet originally was composed of 24 sheets 26"x39". In process work, 12 sheets 35¼"x58½" with 1-inch margin on two sides, or 36¼"x

59½″ are best suited. A room which may be darkened is necessary. At least a 10-foot ceiling is required. A master board 9½′x10½′ is built against one wall, the board being of beaver board to allow thumb tacks. From the center, rule out and mark twelve squares 35¼″x 58½″. (See Fig. 1.) Also in another color, mark out original sheet sizes, this to allow for laps. The blank sheets are then tacked in place on this board.

The original approved drawing is in miniature size. This is placed into the enlarging camera and focused to the proper size for the sheets on the board. Trace with a soft pencil all lines, marking colors as you go along. When completed you will have 12 original sheets which will require 12 operations or screens for each color. These are mounted on the smooth side of a sheet of beaver board with rubber cement so that they may be removed and the board used again.

The screens are now to be made and several are possible. The simplest is to take transparent tracing paper and trace the color to be run on same. Now cut this first color, placing centers of letters and designs aside, numbering with corresponding numbers of large or original cut sheet. These sheets should be the same size as the poster paper, and if placed on the original traced sheet, will fit all succeeding sheets. When the stencil has been cut, place a sheet of blank poster paper on the printing table. Place the stencil on this, fitting exactly on this poster sheet. Place centers in place. Lower the screen, which should have silk No. 12. Place the paint into the screen and squeegee paint across; this will adhere the stencil to the silk. Scotch tape may be used to hold edges of paper.

The single block-out stencil may also be used wherever the design is sketched on the silk and blocked out with lacquer. This will result in a thinner paint film. The Tusche Method may also be used. Photographic or litho-

graphic crayon screens may be used if not of too great
a surface. Poster paper must be used and should be
regular 60-pound poster type. This has a rough side and
a smooth side. Printing is done on the smooth side. Paint

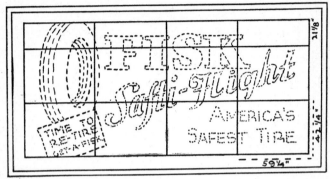

Fig. 2.

should be of a flexible nature and a mixture of ⅓ part
synthetic or long oil type, ⅓ part poster or flat colors, ⅙
part petroleum sistillate, ⅙ part varnish. Transparent
base is added in proportions to the color being run and
also if it goes over another previous color. Never use a
poster color or flat type straight, as it will crack, chalk
or powder. Room temperature is important due to paper
expansion and contraction.

In modern use and now being used are the proportions
as in Fig. 2, namely 8 sheets 59¼"x42¼" and the top
4 sections 21⅛"x59¼". In using this size combination
you will be using a size comparable to many lithographic
standard sizes.

CHAPTER XXXVIII

INDIRECT PHOTOGRAPHIC METHOD

BY indirect Photographic Silk Screen is meant the placing of the light sensitive solution on a supporting sheet, exposing, washing, then attaching to the silk screen, and removing the backup sheet.

First (Fig. 1)—mix ¼ teaspoon Bichromate of Potassium

⅛ teaspoon Bichromate of Ammonia

¼ teaspoon Sugar

1 package Knox Gelatine

Of this mixture take two level teaspoons and mix with two ounces cold water. Let this soak or dissolve for ten minutes. Add 8 ounces of hot water, stirring well, then place in a double boiler (Fig. 2), adding ⅛ teaspoon LePages or Rogers Liquid Glue and ¼ teaspoon vinegar. When this is at the boiling point, remove from the fire and add a pinch of purple dye and ½ ounce methyl alcohol, mix well and strain into a dark bottle.

Take a sheet of celluloid 35/100ths thick, and grease one side (Fig. 3), place this on a piece of glass (Fig. 4), leveling and smoothing with a squeegee. Wax the top of this celluloid sheet, rubbing well. Around the edge of the celluloid place masking tape (Fig. 5), to hold the emulsion from spreading and running over the edges. Next pour the warm emulsion into a tablespoon and pour on the celluloid (Fig. 6). This should be done on a

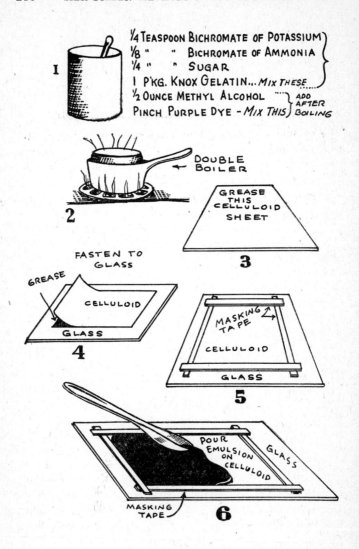

1   ¼ Teaspoon Bichromate of Potassium
    ⅛ "   "   Bichromate of Ammonia
    ¼ "   "   Sugar
    1 P'kg. Knox Gelatin... *Mix These*
    ½ Ounce Methyl Alcohol   ADD AFTER BOILING
    Pinch Purple Dye – *Mix This*

2   DOUBLE BOILER

3   GREASE THIS CELLULOID SHEET

4   FASTEN TO GLASS
    GREASE
    CELLULOID
    GLASS

5   MASKING TAPE
    CELLULOID
    GLASS

6   POUR EMULSION ON CELLULOID
    GLASS
    MASKING TAPE

level surface, and is left to dry. When dry, cut off a piece large enough and peel from the glass, cleaning off surplus grease. Now place your positive into the exposure frame (Fig. 7), emulsion side up. Then place the piece of sensitized celluloid emulsion to the positive or face down (Fig. 8); on top of this place a piece of carpet padding (Fig. 9); on top of this a thin board lined with felt (Fig. 10), and last put your clamp back in position (Fig. 11). It is now ready for exposing or baking (Fig. 12). With a photoflood bulb expose as follows:

Distance of Bulb to Glass	Exposure	Size of Positive
8 inches	5 minutes	12 sq. inches
9 inches	8 minutes	18 sq. inches
10 inches	10 minutes	24 sq. inches

It is now ready for washing. Remove from frame and take a pan, fill it with warm water (about 90 degrees) adding 1 teaspoon baking soda (Fig. 13). Wash the emulsion until the design is clear and no more color comes away. Lay this on a flat surface and take a frame with new silk that is washed with the water that the celluloid has been washed in (Fig. 13). This is then carefully placed on the sensitized sheet and left to dry (Fig. 14). When dry, remove the celluloid backup sheet. The screen should be washed with lacquer thinner before running the color or after the celluloid is removed.

SUPER DURA SENSITIZED PREPARED SHEETS

There is on the market a new improvement in the Photographic silk screen field, viz., a sheet of celluloid upon which an emulsion is affixed. This is not affected by light until treated with a spirit sensitizer. These materials are contained in small capsules and are dissolved in water. The top of the celluloid is swabbed with this emulsion and is then light-sensitive to strong

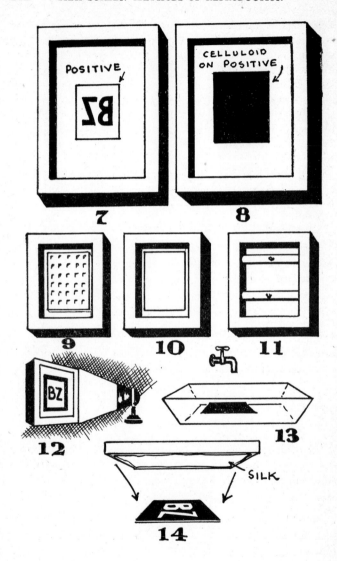

lights, but is not affected by ordinary daylight or ordinary home types of illumination. It is necessary, however, to use the portion of the sheet that has been treated with the emulsion at once as it will not keep for any length of time. It is exposed as other photographic methods in the photo frame and is ready to develop.

To develop, use warm water, temperature at 110 to 120 degrees F. Submerge sheet, then place on a piece of glass or any flat material and flow water over sheet out of a container until the image is clear and the water flowing off the sheet shows no trace of the purple dye. When all trace of the purple dye has disappeared from the water flowing off the sheet, it is an indication that all the soluble material has been washed free. The film is now ready to adhere to the silk.

Place the developed sheet on a perfectly flat surface, such as a piece of plate glass. Lower the silk frame over the design so that the film is placed on the proper area of the silk. Now with newspaper or a soft blotter, press the sheet firmly against the silk and blot up all excess water to hasten the drying of the material. To speed up drying, use an electric fan. When dry, the celluloid sheet will fall away from the design.

CLEANING PHOTOGRAPHIC SOLUTION FROM SCREENS
TO RECLAIM SILK

After paint is thoroughly removed and screen cleaned, soak in hot water for 30 minutes. Dip a brush into a sodium hypochlorite solution and scrub the emulsion side of the silk not over one minute. Immediately wash in clear warm running water (household bleaching solutions may be used). The commercial type of sodium hypochlorite must be diluted with 5 parts water to 1 part solution.

CHAPTER XXXIX

CARBON TISSUE METHOD (Wet)

OBTAIN a piece of Murphy #94 carbon tissue.
1.—Mix the following sensitizing bath, into 25 ounces of distilled or rain water, mix ½ ounce of bichromate chromate potassium, ¼ ounce bichromate of ammonia, 20 grains of carbonate soda, ½ dram ammonia hydrate, ½ ounce methyl alcohol and ¾ ounce sulphuric ether. Into this bath, dip the carbon tissue for 3 minutes (Fig. 1). The pan should be earthen or glass.

2.—Obtain a piece of nitrate base celluloid 3/1000 of an inch thick; this is sandpapered with a No. 3 sandpaper, wiped and polished clean with the regular wax (Fig. 2). It is left to season over night.

3.—Wash the waxed side of the celluloid with a rag saturated with the sensitizing solution (Fig. 3).

4.—Place this sensitized tissue, face or emulsion side toward and on the waxed side of the celluloid (Fig. 4). This and future work should be done in a dark room with a subdued or red light. The sheet is leveled and evened, being lightly squeegeed to remove air, bubbles and surplus water.

5.—Place this between two pieces of glass, weight and leave for 15 minutes (Fig. 5).

6.—Take your photo frame and place it flat on a table, put your positive, whether photographic, line or hand drawn on the glass with the emulsion or copy side up (Fig. 6).

214

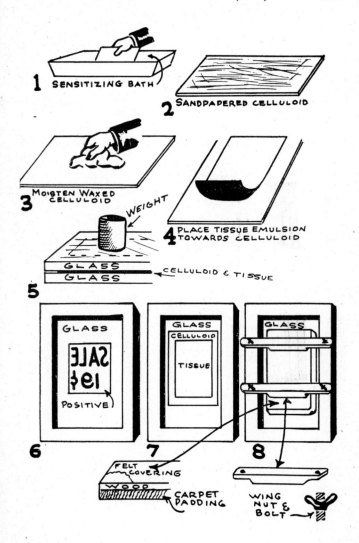

1 SENSITIZING BATH

2 SANDPAPERED CELLULOID

3 MOISTEN WAXED CELLULOID

WEIGHT

4 PLACE TISSUE EMULSION TOWARDS CELLULOID

GLASS
GLASS ← CELLULOID & TISSUE

5

GLASS
SALE 19¢
POSITIVE

6

GLASS
CELLULOID
TISSUE

7

GLASS

8

FELT COVERING
WOOD
CARPET PADDING

WING NUT & BOLT →

7.—On top of this, place the celluloid with the tissue mounted to same, celluloid against the positive, the paper side of the tissue up (Fig. 7).

8.—On top of this place your backup board, which is made of a piece of wood to fit inside of the photo frame, to this is fastened a piece of carpet padding such as is used beneath carpets and the entire piece, wood, padding and all is covered with a piece of felt. The back clamps are then fastened, as perfect contact is essential (Fig. 8).

9.—The lights may now be turned on. To the front of the glass around the edge of the tissue portion, place four pieces of scotch masking tape (Fig. 9).

10.—It is now ready for exposing or baking. Place a #2 photoflood bulb 30 inches from the photo frame and expose from 15 to 18 minutes. Only tests will determine the exact exposure time. (See expose test chart end of this chapter). An electric fan should be trained on the glass, as this will prevent the heat of the lamp from crystallizing the tissue (Fig. 10).

11.—The water for the bath should be between 65 to 70 degrees. Darken the room, remove the celluloid and tissue from the photo frame and place into this bath (Fig. 11), soak it for 5 minutes and then gradually warm the water to about 115 degrees. This should take about 4 or 5 minutes. Slowly from one side, lift the backup sheet of paper from the celluloid (Fig. 12). The emulsion will or should be attached to the celluloid. Wash this back and forth, never touching the emulsion with the fingers until the pattern or design is clear and clean. Remove from the bath and take a pitcher of clean tepid water and rewash.

12.—Place this celluloid, emulsion side up, on to a flat level table and carefully place the silk screen on this. (It is well to wash the screen lightly with a rag saturated with the water that you used as a bath). The frame is then weighted and left to dry. It must be remem-

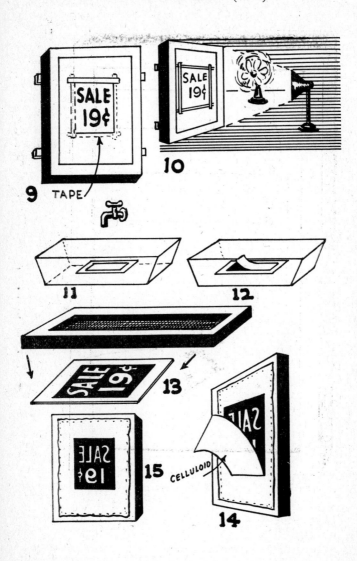

9 TAPE

10

11 12

13

14 CELLULOID

15

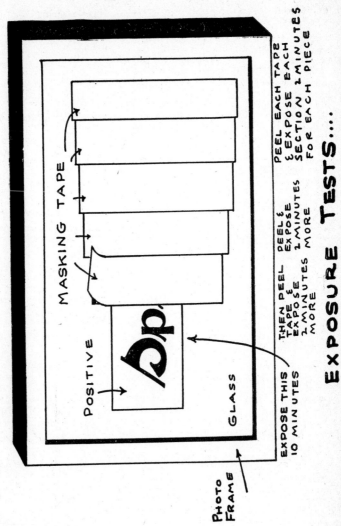

EXPOSURE TESTS....

bered that the celluloid must be smaller than the inside of the frame to assure perfect contact (Fig. 13).

13.—When dry, remove the celluloid backup sheet (Fig. 14).

14.—Wash the screen, tissue and all, with lacquer thinner. Fill the edges with a block out lacquer, tape the back and inside, and the screen is ready for use. This type of screen can be used for all types of color except water colors.

CHAPTER XL

LITHOGRAPHIC OR TUSCHE SCREENS

THE use of lithographic crayon or tusche as a means of obtaining shaded or dot effects with silk screen is possible with the following formula.

The silk screen should be a new piece of silk. The original drawing (Fig. 1), is placed beneath this silk screen on the frame. The various shadings are drawn with a fine pen and India ink directly on the silk (Fig. 2). When the entire drawing has been traced, lift the screen from the drawing and place a piece of sandpaper, mottled cardboard, ben day screen or any irregular surface beneath the silk. The pattern or surface that is placed beneath the silk will be the portions or pattern that will be reproduced.

With a piece of Korns' lithographic crayon #3 (if this is unobtainable, crayola will do the work) trace or draw that portion to be shaded with the crayon (Fig. 3). The depth or strength of pressure used with the crayon will regulate the amount of color or intensity of color. When this is finished, raise the screen from the pattern and with a fine lining or lettering brush stripe in with Korns' Liquid Tusche the straight lines. This is then left to dry, which usually takes about half an hour to one hour.

Mix the following solution: 60% of LePage's or Rogers glue and 40% distilled water. To this add approximately four to five drops of glycerine to the pint. When this has been properly mixed it is strained through a thin

FIG. 1   FIG. 2

FIG. 3

piece of silk or cloth. The screen is then raised off the table level so that it is not touching anything. The glue solution is then placed in a corner of the screen, and with a level piece of cardboard or a very sharp squeegee, squeegee this glue across the top of the silk over the crayon and tusche. Do this two or three times in one period or session. Do not let the glue dry before going over the second or thrid time. This is left to dry, after which it is placed on an ordinary desk blotter. On the inside of the screen, place a piece of newspaper or other absorbent paper, and with a hot flatiron proceed to go over the top of this newspaper (Fig. 4). This will melt the crayon

FIG. 4

and drop it into the blotter, as well as into the newspaper.

If by any chance it will be found that all of the tusche or crayon has not been removed from the screen, it is suggested that one side of the screen be given a coating of turpentine and the other a coating of kerosene or petroleum distillate. It is then washed with a soft brush or soft rag very lightly on both sides with kerosene. It will be found that this will remove all of the tusche or crayon. It is however, not suggested to use this too much as it will have a tendency to chip the edges of the glue.

Many various shades and effects can be obtained by the use of various pattern sheets beneath the silk. It may be suggested that a ben day double deep etch tint plate be obtained from a photo engraver. This placed beneath the screen will give an unusual effect and is very efficient and practical. A designed or embossed cardboard may be used as a pattern beneath the silk. Wire cloth, wire mesh, sandpaper, leather fabric, wood graining, etc., may also be duplicated this way by placing it beneath the screen. Silk should never be coarser than No. 16.

CHAPTER XLI

MECHANICAL MACHINES FOR PROCESS PRINTING

THE COLORGRAPHIC OR ROCKER SCREEN PRESS

T HIS silk screen machine on a flat bed principle is an important development in the silk screen industry. The silk screen is similar to those being used for regular

silk screen reproduction except that the two side pieces of wood which comprise the frame are bowed or bent to allow the screen to release from the printed surface immediately after the squeegee. It is automatic feed in that the automatic gripper feeders feed the paper onto the suction plate bed. The squeegee is of the "A" type, the paint riding between the two blades. This machine is capable of turning out 1800 to 2200 impressions per hour. A conveyor carries the printed cards to either a drying rack or packing room.

CARNALL STENCIL PRINTERS FOR TEXTILE PRINTING

These machines are built to print textile yard goods in

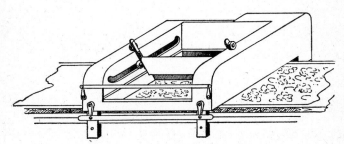

Fig. 1. Model T.

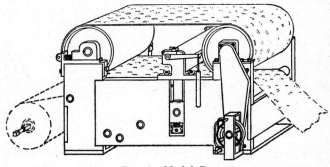

Fig. 2. Model B.

either coated or uncoated form, providing a method using regular silk stencils to produce continuous design with speed and accuracy.

Model T consists of a printing head only. The table

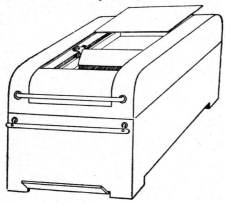

FIG. 3. Model D.

has to be built to order depending on size and length needed. In many cases this can be constructed from materials available in the customer's plant. Tables furnished by this company are constructed of metal with wood top felt padded in twelve foot sections.

Model B consists of three rolls supported in an angle iron frame complete with stretcher, cloth travel rolls, let off, squeegee scrapers, and belt. This machine is limited in designs to regular cut stencils such as dots or broken lines, and designs made up from a series of dots and applies a very heavy deposit of lacquer excellent for flock or bronze printing.

CARNALL STENCIL PRINTERS: AUTOMATIC
SILK SCREEN PRINTERS

These machines are built to supply a need in the silk screen process field by providing mechanical means to operate a screentype stencil adding speed, accuracy, and character not possible with hand operated units.

Model D is equipped with an automatic screen release and starter. When the squeegee reaches the end of its

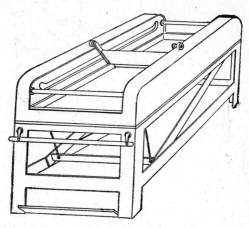

FIG. 4. Model A.

travel, the screen opens and when the screen is closed the squeegee starts, making a full automatic cycle.

Model A is equipped with a lever operating the starting and stopping of the squeegee and the screen is released by a foot-operated lever. The screen is returned to its printing position by hand.

CHAPTER XLII

PAINTS USED IN SCREEN WORK

THE process industry has undergone many changes and developments in the past ten years with the development and introduction of the photographic method of preparing screens, the invention of power driven presses, the speeding up of production, and many other lesser items, but the outstanding advancements have been in the development of paints for process work. Since the founding of the process industry the problem of getting satisfactory paints has been the greatest for the processor. He has had to use makeshift materials prepared from paints, inks, japans, and oil colors, manufactured for different purposes, or make his own colors. The processor would never know if the paints he had prepared would be satisfactory in the way of clogging, dry properly or with a uniform finish, lift the paints over which they were applied, stand die cutting, or fill the many more requirements necessary of a process paint. He had many materials that had to be used as mixtures to keep his paints working properly, and often after this doctoring, would have a paint that was too thin for screening. It is now possible to purchase a paint to fill any requirement the processor may have, whether it be for acid resist or an exterior paint for twenty-four sheet poster work.

Several of the larger manufacturers have set up departments devoted entirely for the development of process material, employing competent screen process experts to work with their technicians on all problems that arise in process shops. They test their colors in process departments, making certain that the materials perform satisfactorily before being made available to the trade. These materials have been developed to the point where they can be used directly from the package without having to add the several reducers, retainers and varnishes that previously were necessary.

With the silk screen process adaptable on practically all surfaces and each individual surface such as parchment, foil coated papers, decalcomania papers, cardboard, wood, glass, all metallic surfaces, canvas, sweater material as with flocked letters, felt, silk, oil cloth and pyroxelin drill, presenting different requirements it is impossible to make a complete line of materials for each item. To meet these problems the paint manufacturers have developed several types of paints that are adaptable for more than one use, by making an addition of a special material which changes its properties and makes it available for another use. In many instances a type of paint is only usable for one surface as with ceramic materials and dye colors for printing design on cloth.

So important is the necessity for good process colors today that it is foolhardy for the average processor to attempt to improvise or manufacture his own materials unless he has had considerable color or paint experience and has kept abreast with the latest developments in the industry. It is true that the prepared process paints are more expensive than those which the processor may have been improvising, but on comparative tests and in working qualities it will be found that they have better opacity and in the end are cheaper to use.

New developments in the pigment field have made new colors available to the processor which before were either impossible to get or too expensive to use, except in small quantities. These colors or pigments are of much cleaner and more brilliant character than colors obtainable before, and are much in demand by the processors of posters. They have been made up in shades that set off their color values to the utmost degree in order to secure the greatest attention value. The colors are of greater color strength and depth and are ideal for shading or producing tints giving the cleanest and richest tones.

Varnishes: Whether they be long oil, short oil, lithol, flatting, or synthetic, the general characteristics they add to a process paint are increasing gloss, except as with flatting varnishes, lengthening the drying time, better and smoother working qualities, prevent clogging, and give the paint better leveling. The addition of special china wood oil varnish produces a faster drying and tougher film than a lithol varnish. A wood oil cumar varnish makes the finish more alkali resistant, and synthetic varnishes give better durilibility on exterior exposure. Care should be taken when making additions of varnishes to process paints, that driers be added to compensate for the increase in drying time, as with lithol varnishes which are very slow drying and will not give good thorough drying for several days unless speeded up with driers.

Reducers or thinners: Each manufacturer has several reducers for each line of paint and it is generally best to use their recommended materials in preference to something the operator may have in his shop and save embarrassing incidents caused by adding the wrong materials, ruining the paint and often the screen. The reducers for flat colors are usually composed of varnishes, sufficient driers for drying at the same rate as the colors and mineral or oleum spirits. The advantage in using the recommended reducer is that it carries the same varnishes as the pastes or colors. Non-clog varnishes are of a heavy bodied nature, and are generally made of lithol varnish, which is a heat bodied varnish. Its slow drying nature has a tendency to slow up fast drying process colors enough to allow them to screen easily and not ruin their fast drying qualities. Care should be taken that an excess of non-clog varnish is never added to flat colors, for this has a great tendency to increase the gloss. Some processors prefer the thinner type reducers. These can be used successfully provided the paint has the necessary working and non-clogging qualities. Oleum spirits, mineral spirits, high flash solvent naphtha and kerosene are the best materials. In high gloss silk screen paints or enamels the only reducers necessary are of the thinner type.

Extender bases: Most process color lines are made up to give complete covering when the colors are super imposed. The only exceptions are in the transparent and production colors which are made for different purposes. If a processor had a one color job to run and had only the strong colors on hand to use, he would be wasting these expensive colors, using them where opacity was not required. In every line of poster colors today, there is included an extender to take the place of admixtures ground in the same vehicle of the same drying qualities. As can be expected, the mixture will not have the same color strength and brilliance as the original color but will retain enough of the color character to be acceptable for this work.

Transparent bases: Many so-called transparent bases are on the market. There are two types of these bases; one made from transparent inerts, such as magnesium carbonate or aluminum hydrate and those made from the metallic soaps, aluminum stearates and palmatates. The first mentioned are more of the type of the extender bases, for they do not produce transparent shades, having a tendency to cloud up the true colors and make them hazy in character, whereas the metallic soaps change the colors in no way. The best test is to screen the transparent base on a sheet of flat black cardboard. If a milky colored film remains when the base is dry, which should be three or four hours after application, the base is made of transparent inerts and is not satisfactory. If no visible residue is left and the transparent base film is very hard to detect, the base has been made from the metallic soaps and is the best obtainable. Transparent base was developed originally for extending the opaque colors in an attempt to produce transparencies for use on lamp shades and similar items where luminous effects were desired. These trials were successful because the opaque pigments were reduced in intensity and dispersed evenly throughout the base to produce a transparent effect. When overprinted, the top color dominated the resultant mixture and the color was not a true transparency. Transparent pigments have been developed which are true tri-chromatic colors, red, blue, and yellow, making possible the most delicate greens and richest purples by either intermixing or over-printing. These pigments which have been incorporated into process pastes have opened a new field to the process industry. For many of the process jobs, a large enough selection of colors is obtainable by running the three colors and black. These four runs make possible a total of fifteen different colors, which doubles the number of colors used on the average job. In the better quality of transparent jobs, a larger number of colors are used. Varying the color strength, having several reds, yellows, blues, and blacks including an intense opaque black for the last run, and by toning the colors with one another, many combinations are obtainable and several thousand tones and shades are possible.

INDEX

Adaptability of Silk Screen
    Process 9
Alizarine lakes 46
Arm-bands, processing 115
Asbestine 41
Attaching silk to frame.... 21

Barytes 41
Base 19
Billboard with imprint..... 94
Blanc fix 41
Blocking the screen....... 52
Blue lakes 46
Brass signs, etched........ 148

Cadmium yellow.......... 43
Carbon black 44
Cement for glass signs.... 149
Charges for process work. 60
Chart of colors........... 49
Chemical colors 41
China wood oil........... 39
Chrome green 43
    yellows 42
Cleaners 40
Clogging of screen........ 62
Coating machine 108
    unit, inexpensive 107
Cobalt blue 44
Color handling 49
    in process work........ 48
    mixing 49
Colors 38, 41
    for glass signs.......... 127
    for outlines and shades.. 104
    ground in oil........... 36
Combination process and
    etched brass signs.... 148
Completed unit, base and
    frame 24

Copy for photographic
    screen 80
Copy, the 51
Cost of seven-color job... 69
Counterbalanced frames... 25
Counter glass signs....... 110
Crimson lakes 45
Cutting letters for stencil. 72
    stencils 15

Decalcomania signs 130
    for trucks and wagons.. 133
Door glass signs.......... 110
Double stencil 14
Dress goods, processing... 117
Driers 40
Drop black 44
Drying rack 32
Dyes 41, 46

Earth colors 41
Elimination process 64
Embossed letter 105
Emerald green 46
Eosin lakes 45
Equipment, arrangement of 57
Equipment for silk screen
    process 19
Estimate for seven-color
    job 69
Estimating the job........ 60
Etched glass signs 122
Etching acid for glass sign 123

Fire red 45
Floating bar, the 21
Flood light box.......... 34
Formula for acid-resisting
    ink 124
Four-color job 77

Four-floating bar frame... 26
Frame 20
  for running glass signs.. 111
  holder 23
  release for 26
  with bridge 95
  with counterweights..... 25
  with grooves 22
Furniture decoration 11

Gelatine solution formula. 91
Gilding device, handy..... 101
Glass, how to polish....... 150
  signs 110, 120
Gold leaf, laying.......... 121
Green lakes 46
Gums 39

Handy shop notes......... 149

Imprints 93
Indian red 42
Ink for glass signs formula 126
Insect spray for lacquer... 144
Iron hydrate 42
  oxides 42
Ivory black 44

Japan colors, use of, in
  screen work 36

Lacquer, use of.......... 144
Lake colors 41, 44
Laminated base 20
Lamp black 44
Letter, shaded 103
Linseed oil 38
Lithographic imprints 93
Lithopone 40
Litho red 45
Luminous white paint..... 150

Markers 29
  placing 52
Master sketch 51
Materials used in process
  work 38
Methods of blocking out.. 68
Mirrors, how to frost..... 149
Mucilage, how to make... 150

Ochre 42
Oilcloth signs, processing.. 116
Oil paper stencil.......... 14
Operation of hand spray.. 146
Orange lake 46
  mineral 43
Orange toner 46
Order of screening colors. 67
Organdy for screens...... 27
  for window backgrounds 113

Packing process cards..... 59
Paint for processing dress
  goods 119
  ideal for process work.. 37
  press 87, 89
  press method of repro-
    duction 87
Paints for glass signs..... 127
  for various materials.... 38
  used in screen work..... 36
Paper cut-out stencil...... 73
  mask stencil 72
  signs 93
Para red 45
Paris green 43
Pennants, processing 115
Photographic screen 80
Pigments 38
Printing inks, use of...... 37
  on curved surfaces...... 151
Processing etched glass
  signs 124
  pennants, arm-bands, etc. 115
  testimonial letters 98
  tire covers 140
  typewritten letters and
    drawings 97
Prussian blue 43
Purity of color........... 41
Purple 46

Rack, drying 32
  for gilded sheets........ 102
  slab 33
Raw materials in paint.... 38
Red lake 45
  oxides 42
Reverse background stencils 16
Rosin 39

Running the job.......... 57

Scarlets 45
Screen, cleaning 57
  clogging 62
  for first color.......... 53
  for second color........ 54
  for glass signs......... 112
  for a slide-off decalco-
    mania 132
  material 27
Screens, preparation of, for
    multicolor jobs 74
Sealing wax, how to make 150
Sensitized screen 80
  screen, frame for....... 82
Sensitizing solution 86
  solution, formula for.... 81
Seven-color job 65
Shaded letter 103
Showcard colors 37
Sienna 41
Silk, attaching 21
  bolting cloth for screens 27
  stretching, the 28
Silvering fluid 150
Single screen process..... 64
  stencil method of repro-
    duction 74
Specification for process
    paint 37
Squeegee, the 30
  for running two-colors at
    once 96
  holders 31
  resharpening 30
Stencil, a two-color....... 18
  designs 145
  double 14
  methods 13
  oil paper 14
  paper mask 72
Stenciling 16
Stencils for the home..... 144
Stick-on letters, how to
    make 101
Stopping out the screen... 52

Stretching the frame...... 28
  the silk 28
Sunlight sign, construction
    of 139
  signs, how to make...... 138
  sign, installation of..... 139
Surfaces, curved or bowl
    shaped 151
  working 107

Taping frame 55
Testimonial letters, pro-
    cessing 98
Thinner for washing screen 54
Three-color lettering job.. 52
Tire covers, processing.... 140
Titanium oxide 41
Toluidine red 45
  toner 45
Trouble shooting 62
Two-color stencils 18
Type matter, to reproduce. 85
Typewritten letters, how to
    process 97

Ultramarine blue 44
Umber 42
Unit ready for copy...... 29
  table 19

Van Dyke brown 42
Vehicles 38
Vellum paper for type-
    written stencils 99
Vermilion 43
Violet 46

White lead, use of 40
Whiting 41
Window backgrounds 113
Wire mesh screen........ 27
Working surfaces 107

Yellow lake 46

Zinc yellow 43
  oxide, use of.......... 40

INDEX—PART II

Acid tank 158
Attaching profilm 178

Bath, sensitising 167
Beeswax 157
Brewery signs 153, 157

Carbon tissue 162
   celluloid for 166
   exposing 164
   washing 166
Celluloid for carbon tissue. 166
Copper plates 164
Crystal lacquer 155
Cutting profilm 174

Etching 154
   solution 154
Exposing carbon tissue.... 164

Glass rack 155
   registering 156
   signs 153

Lacquer, crystal 155
   paper 168
Loose flop stencil 168

Machines, process 187
Mirror outline sign........ 153

Nitrate, silver 154

Outline sign, mirror...... 153

Paper, lacquer 168
Peeling profilm 179
Plates, copper 164

Process machines 187
Process sandblasting 169
Profilm 170
   attaching 178
   cutting 174
   peeling 179
   registering with 180
   removing 183
   surface contact for...... 179

Rack, glass 155
Registering glass 156
   with profilm 180
Removing profilm 183
Resist, sandblast 169

Sandblast resist 169
Sandblasting 169
   process 169
Sensitising bath 167
   solution 163
Sign, mirror outline....... 153
Signs, glass 153
Silk 185
   tacking on 182
Silver nitrate 153
Solution, sensitising 163
   etching 154
Stencil, loose flop........ 168
Surface contact for profilm 179

Tacking on silk........... 182
Tank, acid 158
Tissue, carbon 162
Tusche 160

Washing carbon tissue.... 166

(See Index—Part III on following page.)

INDEX—PART III

Acid etch, white........ 200
Acid, hydrofluoric 195
Acid solution, tartaric.... 196
Adhering Nu-film 190

Back paper, removing... 191
Bar, spanker 202
Base, extender 232
   transparent 232
   bronze, copper or, clean-
    ing 204

Carbon tissue method... 214
Carnell stencil machines. 226
Chart, exposing 212
Charts, test, exposure... 218
Chip etch 195
Cleaning copper or
   bronze 204
   photo screens 213
Compass, cutting 187
Copper electroplated
   screens 200
   or bronze, cleaning.... 204
Cutting 188
   compass 187
   tool 187

Dura sheets, super...... 212

Electroplated screens
   copper 200
Etch, chip 195
   white acid 200
Exposing chart 212
Exposure test charts.... 218
Extender base 232

Finishes, gun metal..... 194
Flock 201
   transparent 203
Flocking yard goods.... 204

Gold mirror formula.... 197
   solution 194
Gun metal finishes...... 194

Hydrofluoric acid 195

Indirect photographic
   method 209

Lithographic or Tusche
   screen 220

Method, carbon tissue... 214
Mirror formula, gold.... 197
   solution, gold 194
   stains, removing 199
   transparent 198

Nu-film 187
   adhering 190

Paint in screen work.... 229
Paper, back, removing.. 191
Photo screens, cleaning. 213
Photographic method, in-
   direct 209
Posters, 24 sheet........ 206
Press, Rockerscreen 225

Reducers and thinners.. 231
Removing back paper... 191
   mirror stains 199
Rockerscreen press 225

Screen, lithographic or
   Tusche 220
Screen work, paint in.... 229
Screens, copper electro-
   plated 200
   photo, cleaning 213
Sheets, super dura....... 212
Spanker bar 202
Stencil machines, Carnell 226
Super dura sheets....... 212

Tartaric acid solution... 196
Test charts, exposure... 218
Thinners 231
Tissue method, carbon.. 214
Tool, cutting 187
Transparent base 232
  flock 203
  mirror 198

Tusche screen, or litho-
  graphic 220
24 sheet posters......... 206

Varnishes 231

White acid etch......... 200

Yard goods, flocking.... 204